THE GOOD DOCTOR GUIDE

A Unique Directory
of Recommended Specialists

Second Edition

MARTIN PAGE

SIMON & SCHUSTER

LONDON·SYDNEY·NEW YORK·TOKYO·SINGAPORE·TORONTO

First published in Great Britain by Simon & Schuster Ltd, 1993
A Paramount Communications Company

Copyright © Martin Page, 1993

Simon & Schuster Ltd
West Garden Place
Kendal Street
London W2 2AQ

Simon & Schuster of Australia Pty Ltd
Sydney

A CIP catalogue record for this book is available from the British Library

ISBN 0–671–71165–2

Typeset in Sabon by SLG Business Services
Printed in Great Britain

Important Note

This book has been researched and compiled in unusually
difficult circumstances imposed by medical regulations
concerning publicity. In particular, these regulations
have prevented the doctors named in this book from being
able to check their own entries. Despite this, every effort
has been made to ensure the accuracy of all entries and
neither the author nor the publisher can accept responsi-
bility for any errors of fact.

The Good Doctor Guide is not a comprehensive work
and the omission of a particular doctor's name is in no way
an adverse reflection on that doctor's skill, actual or
implied.

"Unless we put medical freedom into the constitution, the time will come when medicine will organise into an undercover dictatorship."

– **Dr Benjamin Rush, MD** (Edinburgh, 1768), founder, People's Free Dispensery, Philadelphia; co-founder, American Anti-Slavery League; first Professor of Medicine and Clinical Practice, University of Pennsylvania; author, *Medical Inquiries and Observations* (5 volumes); co-author, US Declaration of Human Rights.

"I do not accept that it can be right in any circumstances to give publicity to a professional person of whatever status without their permission."

– **Sir John Batten, MD** (London, 1951), President, Medical Protection Society.

"A large number of doctors have written to the Association in strong terms to express their strong disapproval of their inclusion in your proposed **Guide.***"*

– **Dr Natalie-Jane Macdonald, MB, BS** (Glasgow, 1984), Head of Ethics and European Affairs, British Medical Association.

*"**The Good Doctor Guide** has reared its ugly head once more, only to have it bitten off by the General Medical Council. And quite right too ... What is particularly worrying is that it has been bought by GPs and patients, who may take the list seriously ... It is hard to grasp what those [doctors who advised Mr Page] hoped to get out of it. Ironically, they now face blacklisting by the profession, if their identities are ever revealed."*

– *Hospital Doctor* magazine.

For Catherine,
who inspired *The Good Doctor Guide*,
and who worked so closely with me
on this second edition.

Many thanks to:

Mat and Sam for their patience.

The management and staff of Hilton's magnificently restored Langham Hotel, just around the corner from Harley Street, for their hospitality during our researches.

Steven Hilton of Alfalogia of Lisbon, for his expert advice in the computer-processing of the data.

The *Evening Standard* Magazine, the *People* and the *Sunday Express*, in which parts of this book have already appeared.

Professor Michael Besser, Professor Karol Sikora, and our other referees, whose concern for the rights of patients has made *The Good Doctor Guide* possible.

CONTENTS

Introduction

Do you need to consult the world's leading expert on amyloidosis (the presence of abnormal proteins in the walls of blood cells)? An artificial elbow? Fine-tuning of hormonal treatment for PMT? To have a kidney removed through a one-centimetre incision? For your child to grow taller, or more slowly? The experimental genetic manipulation of a tumour, to encourage it to consume itself? A neurosurgeon specialising in repairing nerves damaged by orthopaedic surgeons?

In an era when the competence of so many of Britain's once respected institutions is in question, from its monarchy to its schools, from the Bank of England to the Church of England, a survey conducted by the Parisian newspaper *Libération* found that 700 European professors of medicine consider London still to be Europe's unchallenged centre of excellence in clinical innovation.

This is not to disparage Britain's provincial centres of medical excellence. Continental Europe's professors rated Cambridge, Glasgow and Oxford as clinically superior to Munich and Paris.

Despite cuts by successive governments – those announced for 1993 were the twentieth since the Second World War – London also remains, by far, at the time of going to press Europe's largest centre of specialist medicine. If all the planned closures and mergers go through, which is doubtful, there will still be eight mammoth teaching hospitals and seven independent specialist postgraduate hospitals.

The latter include the Royal Postgraduate Medical School in Hammersmith, constantly in the forefront of advance technology; Moorfields, where laser eye surgery began; the Royal Marsden for cancer treatment, and the Royal Brompton National Heart and Lung Hospital.

Over 2,500 doctors of consultant or professorial rank work in and around London. While British medical postgraduates flock to Boston, New York and California, to train for a year or more under specialists there, young doctors from continental Europe flow into London on a similar quest.

The deans of the medical schools have discovered that scores of young German doctors, failing to gain entry through the front door of educational exchange and scholarship programmes, resort to ruses to get in through the back, with the help of their professors and at the British taxpayers' expense.

As patients, foreigners are currently estimated to be spending over £1 billion a year on receiving treatment in London. At current prices, under investigation from the Monopolies and Mergers Commission, this is equivalent to about a quarter of a million hip replacements, or half a million lens implants replacing cataracts.

Most foreign patients are from continental Europe. In 1993, at least three NHS surgical terms, while working privately part-time, in American-owned private hospitals in central London, each carried out more open-heart operations on Europeans of other nationalities than all those undertaken on Finns in Finland.

It is the range, the variety and the constant growth of London's super-specialisation that are its most impressive distinctions, beyond its Nobel prizes and the hundreds of millions of pounds a year its clinical academicians attract in research funds. Where else is one to find in the same town, a physician who specialises in treating kidney failure in relation to hypertension, a colleague in relation to diabetes, and another in relation to auto-allergy?

Here, one surgeon operates on facial nerves, another on salivary glands, a third on tear ducts. Here, too, are world authorities on the medico-legal aspects of altitude sickness, on female sexual deviancy, on male incontinence, on sense of smell, on children's colonoscopy – over a thousand specialities within specialities, created by a fusion of individual and collective ingenuity.

The British themselves pay mostly through taxation for this glittering array of medical expertise. It is now more than ten years since Parliament gave the British the right, always taken for granted in the rest of Europe and in the USA, to consult any doctor, whether generalist or specialist, without first obtaining another doctor's permission. (A specialist whom one consults directly is forbidden by law from informing your GP, if you object to his doing so.)

When one seeks to benefit from this right, through the NHS or privately, one is faced by an extraordinary obstacle. A wall of secrecy about specialists' qualifications, skills and professional repute is maintained, as best they can, by the British Medical Association and the General Medical

Council. Their assertion is that information is bad for you, because you might not be up to understanding it correctly.

Both the BMA and the GMC have exerted considerable energy and effort in attempting to sabotage or at least diminish *The Good Doctor Guide,* precisely because its purpose is to make information easily available to those outside, as well as within, the medical profession.

Among other things, they have repeatedly called into question the motive behind this book. This is not financial. Like many people with an inherited disease – though in my case a relatively minor one, of gradual blindness – I have sometimes had hard thoughts about doctors lacking both in technical competence and in humanity. Also, out of seven operations I had undergone by the age of fifty, conducted by surgeons to whom I had been referred by GPs, three had been failures. In no instance was this fact volunteered by the doctors involved, causing further physical damage. Catherine, my wife, persuaded me to turn away from bitterness, and instead help myself by helping others, by identifying specialists in medicine and surgery of above average competence and, though more difficult to assess, decency.

About The Good Doctor Guide

The Good Doctor Guide identifies specialists who have been chosen by a panel of over fifty senior consultants and professors. The referees are asked two basic questions: To which other doctors in your own and closely related fields would you refer a close relative, and for what conditions? If in doubt over a diagnosis or treatment of a patient of your own, which other doctors would you consult for a second opinion? For a candidate to be included for this guide, a recommendation had to be made by at least two referees, based on their personal knowledge.

The GMC has threatened to take disciplinary action against any doctor who helps in the compilation of the *Guide*. Such help includes a doctor checking his own entry for accuracy. The punishment proposed in the medical press is 'professional blacklisting'.

Two of our referees, however, have volunteered to waive their anonymity, so as to test what these threats amount to in practice. Dr. Michael Besser, the internationally honoured endocrinologist, is Professor of Medicine at St Bartholomew's. Dr Karol Sikora, Professor of Clinical Oncology at the Royal Postgraduate Medical School, Hammersmith, is a pioneer of the genetic treatment of tumours, and chairman of the government's review of cancer treatment in the UK. Neither is responsible for the *Guide*'s contents. Both have nominated doctors for inclusion, in order to endorse, on ethical grounds, freedom of information for patients and their relatives about clinicians.

This new edition of *The Good Doctor Guide* has been completely revised, updated and expanded since the *Guide*'s first edition in 1989, both in the number of entries and sections. This reflects both the continuing growth of our panel of senior professional referees and some remarkable clinical advances – not least in minimally intrusive surgery and in pain control.

The number of specialist sections has increased from forty to sixty-nine and includes twenty-one specifically dedicated to children. More than 200 of the doctors named are included for the first time. Furthermore, a list of seventy outstanding provincial specialists, though not identified by the *Guide*'s usual sources, is published later in this introduction.

Most of the doctors whose names were in the first edition, but are not in this one, have retired. Two have died of AIDS (caught in neither case from a patient, and neither of them practising in HIV/AIDS clinics). Another was 'erased from the Register' by the GMC, not for incompetence – it rarely disciplines doctors on such grounds – but after being exposed in the press for transplanting kidneys which had been bought from live donors, impoverished Third World peasants. This has provoked some ethical debate as to whether the GMC was not transgressing the peasants' civil rights. Other doctors previously named are missing from this edition only because our referees had no recent knowledge of their clinical performance. There has been no blackballing of doctors.

The *Guide* does not aspire to be a comprehensive work. It includes doctors whose work is known recently to, and is highly regarded by, those of their peers who advise us. We emphasise strongly that the omission of a doctor's name in no way reflects adversely on him or her.

About the Medical Bureaucracy

Two bodies have sought to obstruct or diminish *The Good Doctor Guide*'s publication, the BMA and the GMC. The BMA's opposition, if not the ethics of all its tactics, is the more understandable.

Contrary to widespread public assumption, the BMA has no official status. It is but a trade union. Most general practitioners belong to it, but only a minority of consultants and professors. The BMA's fear is that if patients are given access to information about specialists, they may consult them directly, instead of through a BMA member. Thus, the BMA perceives the *Guide* as a threat to "referral", its members' restrictive practice, which has been in place for the past century and a half.

In the BMA's published attacks on the *Guide*, it has described it as "bad news for patients". Its argument is that a patient, unless steered by a GP, may go to the wrong specialist. The implication is not only that, unguided, we might go to an ENT surgeon with an eye problem, or seek treatment for asthma from a gynaecologist. It is also that specialists are so roguish and deceitful, and so hungry for patients, they might not let on that they weren't the right doctor for the job.

It seems unreasonable to be other than open-minded about the value, from the patient's point of view, of referral to a specialist through a general practitioner. If one is satisfied with one's GP, as is now the case in my family, it is natural that one would seek his or her advice. All too often, however, it is dissatisfaction with their GP that determines patients to consult a specialist.

Seeing a specialist may also be the patient's only chance of having a doctor spend sufficient time examining his condition. A GP may seek to get through a consultation in under five minutes. Whatever the shortcomings of Harley Street, there a patient tends to be given at least half an hour and often, initially, an hour.

Proponents of the cartel arrangement point out that it is important that a specialist is given an overall view of the patient's medical condition and background. Undeniably, it is part of the fundamental role of a GP to provide this information. Specialists, however, habitually complain that it is a role in which many GPs fail as a matter of routine. I opened the envelope containing a note written about me from a GP to a consultant ophthalmologist. It read: "This big chap says he has trouble with his eyes."

The cartel arrangement is a peculiarity of British medicine. It has no parallel in the USA or in continental Europe, nor is there pressure abroad from the public or the profession to institute one. So far from making the role of the GP obsolete, their standing in public esteem there seems markedly higher than in Britain. As for demand for their services, under freedom of patients' choice, there is a recorded shortage of GPs in America.

It appears to be the view of the BMA that its members might not fare so well in similar conditions, and that they depend for their livelihoods in part on maintaining public ignorance.

Under current British law, a patient is not obliged to obtain his GP's permission to see a consultant. Open information about specialists can only help a patient and his GP to come to a shared decision. Now that so many GPs allocate state funds for the specialist treatment of patients registered with them, the need for patients to be better informed about the options is all the more evident.

The General Medical Council's opposition to *The Good Doctor Guide* is more controversial. The GMC is a statutory body, established by Parliament to regulate medical practice in Britain in the interests of patients. Its concept of its duties in this matter is remarkably restricted, by international standards. In Portugal, for example, two casualty officers who delayed treating a road accident victim in need of neurosurgery, under pressure of work, were given prison sentences, only suspended on appeal. In May 1993, a psychiatrist who remarked to a homosexual patient that he only had himself to blame for contracting AIDS was quickly and publicly censured by the Medical Council for his callousness. This is no more perhaps slightly less, than would happen in other countries. In a recent year, the GMC received over 100 complaints from or on behalf of patients, alleging clinical ill-treatment by doctors on its register. Every one of these complaints was rejected without a hearing by the GMC, in "preliminary screening".

The complaints were not only from lay people. One came

from a council member of the Royal College of Obstetricians and Gynaecologists and head of the obst and gyn department at one of London's major teaching hospitals. He wrote to urge the GMC to reconsider its refusal to act on the concern already expressed to it by other doctors, regarding the qualifications and psychological fitness of Dr Thomas Courtenay to practise in the speciality.

Before establishing himself in Harley Street as a gynaecologist, Dr Courtenay had been in Dublin. He had left because he had fallen into deep professional disgrace soon after taking his degree. Before his arrest, conviction and imprisonment in London as a serial rapist, police believe he sexually violated over 100 women in his consulting rooms.

Under the GMC's aegis, the protection of patients in Britain lags perhaps half a century behind that of the rest of the Western world. One of the ways in which it does so is that, uniquely, a doctor can call himself a gynaecologist, or a practitioner in any other speciality, without training or qualification in it. Anywhere else in Europe, as in the USA, Dr Courtenay would have been tried and convicted by the regulatory body, for quackery, at the outset.

In representing himself to be a specialist when he was not, he was committing no offence in Britain or in the eyes of the GMC. After his imprisonment, we surveyed a sample of over 250 doctors practising in Harley Street. More than a quarter of them were not accredited or qualified in any speciality.

Only doctors who are fully qualified and accredited in their specialities are considered for inclusion in *The Good Doctor Guide.* Yet the GMC says that people who are ill, and those close to them, may not be in a mentally fit state to take in such information, and that it should therefore not be disclosed publicly. When it learned of the *Guide's* first edition from newspaper reports, shortly before its publication, the GMC wrote to the publisher urging that the book be cancelled, unless evidence could be produced to disprove the implicit guilt of the specialists whose names were printed in it. Otherwise, they might be deprived by the GMC of their professional status and their livelihoods.

After publication, the GMC sent letters to every specialist listed (those mentioned twice, in different sections, received two letters), advising them to protest against being described as good doctors, and enclosing a proposed text. Out of almost 500, about 120 complied. Of those, over 100 kept virtually, word for word, to the dictated pro forma. Some sent separate messages, saying that they had complied under duress. An impression had been created that, had they not done so, their professional liability insurance might be in jeopardy.

The basis of the GMC's campaign thinking seems to have been that it is against its rules to praise a doctor in print, without first seeking and receiving his consent. Under its rules, a specialist must always deny such consent. So, by the GMC's logic, there could not be a second edition of *The Good Doctor Guide*. In a letter, it claimed that the government "strongly supported" this strategy. *Hospital Doctor* magazine announced that the guide had "bitten the dust" and could not now appear again.

The BMA also launched a campaign to have specialists I had praised send nasty letters to my home address, which it circulated. Six out of 100 responded – one of them to warn of what was afoot, one to give his correct NHS address, one to say she was about to retire, two pointing out they had just been promoted from senior lecturers to professors.

In its rule book for the medical profession, the GMC already claimed the power, ostensibly conferred on it by Lord Justice Scrutton in 1930, to impose its rules "written and unwritten". It now introduced a specific regulation, making it "serious misconduct", punishable by "erasure from the Register", for a specialist not to demand the erasure of his name from a selective guide to medical practitioners.

We took specialist legal opinion in 1993. It was that both in its new regulation, and in threatening doctors over it, the GMC was breaking the law. At the time of going to press, the GMC was disputing this. (Meanwhile, to encourage more openness in British society, the government had placed in the public domain the name, and specifications of the training, qualifications and personal background, of the director of MI5.)

A particular illusion the GMC has created about itself is that it forbids medical advertising. If one means by "advertising", as it has been commonly understood to mean since the sixteenth century, "a paid announcement", this is untrue. Magazines, newspapers and radio stations in Britain habitually carry advertisements offering specialist medicine and surgery in a variety of fields. These include, as well as cosmetic surgery, gynaecology and obstetrics, ophthalmology, psychiatry and urology.

The dodge, to which the GMC casts a cynically acquiescent eye, is that these advertisements are not placed by doctors directly, but by medically unqualified intermediaries, whom the doctors retain to recruit patients. A few of the advertisers are reputable private hospitals, whose managers do not give facilities to doctors who are not fully qualified and accredited consultants. King Edward VII's Hospital, long patronised by royalty, publishes and freely distributes an advertising pamphlet giving the Harley Street addresses and phone numbers of the freelance specialists who use its premises. Most of the advertising, however, is by freelance agents in rented offices, some in Harley Street, working on commission for surgeons who may not be fully qualified and accredited, and which may not necessarily act in the patients' best interests.

The GMC's rule that specialists must do everything they can to suppress editorial coverage of their work, if it might attract prospective patients, has also been almost entirely ignored by the GMC itself. In the year ending March 1993, more than 200 reports about clinical innovations were published in national newspapers. In each case, the specialist responsible was named, and his professional whereabouts stated. Almost all these reports were based on information supplied by the specialists.

What the GMC seems to fear is the publication of independently researched and collated information about specialists' skills and particular interests, for the use of people outside, as well as within, the medical profession.

Until the first edition of *The Good Doctor Guide* was published in 1989, it was widely assumed that it was illegal to publish such information. It was thought that the GMC had supralegal powers of censorship over what was published about doctors, much as the D-Notice Committee kept militarily sensitive information from being printed or broadcast.

This assumption seems to have been shared by some members of the GMC itself. In the most recent edition of its rules (May 1992) it continued the confusion by still claiming jurisdiction over the provision of information "about doctors and their services".

Its powers are intended rather to restrict hype by doctors about their services. In this, as already noted, it appears to have been negligent.

In its current rule book, the GMC endorses the method by which this *Guide* is compiled, peer referral, "if it is intended to promote the best interests of patients". Its objection is to the recommendations being made available to patients, so they can judge their best interests for themselves.

Who's Got to the Top in London Medicine?

Of the doctors listed in this edition, only six – just over 1 per cent – are in full-time private practice. This proportion may increase, of course, if the government carries out further swingeing cuts. For the time being, the top doctors' sense of commitment to the NHS and to academic clinical research is notable.

Sixty-eight are professors. Most accept some private patients, but many still refuse to profit personally from doing so, passing on the fees to their research funds.

Almost a quarter of the professors and consultants listed have undertaken postgraduate training and/or research in the USA. Fewer than five appear to have done so in Europe.

Forty-four per cent of them first qualified as doctors in London itself. By far the leading source of recruiting from elsewhere is Cambridge, from where ninety-six of the top doctors graduated. The vast majority of these are physicians, rather than surgeons.

Oxford comes next with thirty-one, about equally divided between physicians and surgeons. Twenty come from Scotland, twelve from Birmingham, ten from Liverpool, six from Dublin, five each from Belfast and South Africa – the overwhelming majority of these are surgeons. The four from Bristol are all physicians.

Australia, Leeds, Manchester, Newcastle and New Zealand field three each, and Cardiff two.

Baltimore, Bombay, Buenos Aires, Colombo, Durham and Liège are represented by one each. Marc de Leval, the Belgian paediatric heart surgeon, is the only representative from all the rest of the European Community. Few think this reflects anything but xenophobia at the top of British medicine.

The number of women in this elite has almost doubled since the last edition of *The Good Doctor Guide*, to twenty-eight, or approaching 5 per cent. Whatever the reasons for this still very small percentage, it reflects a severe insensitivity to the market for specialist medicine. Many female patients who wish to consult a gynaecologist of the same sex, or a woman paediatrician about their children, are still deprived of a realistic opportunity to do so. If the problem is the hours involved in training as a specialist, during a women's child-bearing and -raising years, then it is surely the system and not the customer that is wrong.

"Not a Trade, but a Learned Profession": Doctors' Earnings

Few incomes are as fabled and, sometimes, as begrudged as those of London's top doctors. Here, at its most opulent, is a world of Rolls-Royces with personalised number plates, estates in Wiltshire and ski chalets in Switzerland.

The King's Fund claimed in 1992 that the most successful consultants earned, on average, almost £200,000 a year each. Its William Laing commented archly that how this is being achieved "without compromising their NHS service is a conundrum which has not yet been satisfactorily answered".

The nudge and the wink is that such doctors are enriching themselves by cheating the NHS. This is true in a few cases. In the great majority, the truth is the opposite, and the way in which patients are in danger of being let down is more alarming.

By long tradition, and to the enduring irritation of politicians and hospital managers, consultant physicians and surgeons are self-employed, and on freelance contracts with the NHS. Such contracts are for a certain number of half-day sessions a week. On that basis, consultants argue, it is their private work that subsidises the NHS.

Commonly, they give the NHS many more hours a week than those contracted, often including evening and weekend work. Their working conditions are often minimal – in many a major teaching hospital, a head of department's "office" is a cupboard in a corridor. They do not claim from the NHS expenses to which they are entitled. They teach the next generation of specialists without fee.

By his early fifties, a consultant physician – a gastroenterologist, a chest expert, a neurologist – in a top London teaching hospital may be earning £40,000 from the NHS, for thirty hours a week: about £28 an hour, before tax. By his calculation, this is modest: less than his accountants charge for keeping his books.

In his private practice, he bills his time at an average of £100 an hour: more up front, for an initial consultation, less for time involved in consequent treatment. From his private practice, he reckons to gross around £90,000 a year, with expenses of about £30,000.

By the standards of the fees charged by the City solicitors

he treats, this is derisory. The physician maintains his professional superiority, when consulted by prominent barristers over medical litigation, by having them attend him in his Harley Street room, rather than going to see them in their chambers.

Top surgeons earn much more than consultant physicians, up to £300,000 a year in their private practices. The threat that they will take their scalpels to a greater fortune in the USA is largely a hollow one, because few want to move there with their families.

Foreign surgeons working here – Great Ormond Street's Marc de Leval from Belgium, Moorfield's Arthur Steele from Australia – could earn much more if they returned to whence they came, but prefer to be on the front edge, in London.

Some English surgeons argue that their work for the NHS is an act of charity. An orthopaedic surgeon reckons he charges the NHS £15 for a hip or knee replacement, compared with £600 for a similar operation privately. The BMA's recommended charge is £700. This surgeon, charging at the lower BUPA scale of £100 less, reckons that if he went private full-time, he could earn in a fortnight what he takes from the NHS over a year.

The danger this situation is creating is not that consultants are skiving, but that they are overworking. On their way in their BMWs from their NHS hospitals to their private ones, during the lunch half-hour, they eat a yoghurt and an apple, while briefing secretaries and assistants on their car phones.

Surgeons leave home on Monday at 6.30 a.m. to be in the theatre at 7.30, and return home at 11.00 p.m. to watch *News at 10,* which their wives have video-recorded for them, before going to bed. Their marriages break up. They are given weekend access to their children. These, they take on their Sunday ward rounds, before returning them to their mothers and starting a new week.

Among London's medical elite, there is a macho ethic of never being tired. This is the danger posed to NHS and private patients alike.

The Decline of Harley Street

For more than a century, Harley Street has been to private
medicine what King's Cross is to whores, Cork Street is to
art dealers, and Fleet Street was to journalists. Today, its
sprouting "To Let" signs signify more than recession. If
and when recovery begins, the new generation of specialists
will not be signing up for the leases.

In better times, Lord Howard de Walden and his family,
the principal landlords, could be picky about the tenants
and still count on making £6 million a year. At the top end
of the street, by Regent's Park, newly appointed consultants
rented rooms by the hour in what were known as "warm-
couch" houses. The doorman slotted in and out their name-
plates as they came and went.

Down the street, towards Coutts Bank's medical branch,
some of London's older consultants rent – often sharing
with a colleague – suites costing perhaps £35,000 a year to
run. But as they retire, few younger doctors seem interested
in taking their places. They conduct the administration of
their private practices from home, with part-time secretaries, often their wives. They see their private patients in
consulting rooms in the private hospitals in which they
intend to admit them. By my estimation, a quarter of the
reputable specialists who were practising in Harley Street in
1989 have quit for elsewhere.

Commercially run hospitals, many American-owned,
like the Princess Grace Hospital, the Portland Hospital
for Women and Children, the Cromwell and the Humana
Hospital Wellington, offer on-the-spot X-rays, ultrasound and laboratory tests – facilities few Harley Street
practices have.

This one-stop approach to diagnosis and treatment has
been the norm in continental Europe for years. Its introduction to London is bad news for the de Waldens, but
welcome to arthritics who no longer have to hobble up and
down Harley Street, from rheumatologist to orthopaedic
consultant, from X-ray to imaging centre, from acupunc-
turist to physiotherapy pool, and back again.

A Question of Degrees

It is not only because of Britain's growing lack of confidence in its own excellence that medical consultants, as a tribe, are not always held in esteem. Another factor is that they know, and they are known to, few beyond their own circle. This, together with their penchant for expensive cars, clothes, houses, holidays and wines, can make them front-row coconuts in political shies. The current system of training and preferment, and its extraordinary demands on their time, has also isolated them from the rest of us.

In the rest of the European Community, over the past fifteen years, there has been a continuing reassessment of how best to create future specialists. The non-British consensus is that, with new high-tech methods of teaching as well as treatment, a doctor should be competent to perform operations such as gall-bladder removal, replacement of cataracts with lens implants, and of arthritic hips with artificial ones, after eight years of properly planned tuition in a university hospital.

A new generation of deans of medicine in Britain is trying to put through reforms to make their hospitals less like sweatshops for junior specialists in training. But the GMC and the medical royal colleges have resisted any curtailment in training time, effectively keeping it at about double that demanded abroad. The demands on an aspirant hospital doctor are so high, and his salary so low, that he is almost entirely cut off from the world, other than his colleagues and patients, until he is well into middle age.

The misunderstandings are, of course, compounded by doctors' archaic traditions of secrecy. No other profession, nor any other medical hierarchy in the world, has as many or as high degrees and formal qualifications, or does less to make clear to patients and the rest of the public what they mean.

The confusion is such that it is widely supposed that a 'Mr' is senior to a 'Dr'. In private practice, the former usually earns considerably more per hour, but may be no better qualified, only differently.

For the customer, the letters after a doctor's name are an initial snare. A Member of the Royal College of Surgeons (MRCS) has merely passed half the exams required for him to become a houseman and then to go on to further training to become a GP.

A Member of the Royal College of Physicians (MRCP), on the other hand, has achieved his diploma through perhaps seven years of relentlessly hard study, research and clinical training after first qualifying. This diploma distinguishes a physician from a GP. In surgery the equivalent is a Fellow of the Royal College of Surgeons (FRCS).

A doctor becomes an FRCS or an MRCP through examination and clinical proficiency. On passing – the failure rate in both is high – an FRCS reverts to being a 'Mr', while an equally ranked physician, with an MRCP, remains a 'Dr'.

To become a Fellow of the Royal College of Physicians (FRCP), a doctor has to have made in the estimation of his seniors what the college calls 'a substantial impact on medicine', and it is a distinction not lightly conferred.

A Member of the Royal College of Obstetricians and Gynaecologists (MRCOG) becomes a Fellow almost as a matter of routine after about five years. A growing consensus in the Royal College of Physicians believes that this is the better system.

The GMC now permits GPs to publish pamphlets stating their qualifications. Few if any GPs have doctorates. The title of doctor is a courtesy one, an unearned politeness from the rest of us. This is in no way reprehensible since they are as well qualified as their colleagues abroad who sport the initials MD, except that it devalues the English degrees of MD and DM, which some universities rank as academically higher than doctorates (PhDs) in other subjects.

A GP may have printed after his name the initials MB, BS and LRCP, MRCS. This is, from the customer's point of view, a potentially misleading repetition. Both sets of qualifications are identical in the eye of the GMC, the one achieved by passing university exams, the other through parallel ones set by the royal colleges. To have one without the other is as good as having the two. Some doctors have both because they were advised by their teachers at medical school to sit the two exams, for fear that they might fail one of them.

The formal qualification that distinguishes the more dedicated GPs from the rest is membership, then fellowship, of the Royal College of General Practitioners (RCGP). This is not a compulsory qualification. The college is of comparatively recent origin, but it is getting difficult to join any of the more prosperous general partnerships without belonging to it.

At present, specialists cannot become NHS consultants without first obtaining the appropriate degrees, diplomas, memberships and fellowships and royal-college accreditation. Their paths divide from those of future GPs on completing their 'house training' (six months of medicine and six months of surgery in an approved hospital).

A Quick Guide to the Letters After Doctors' Names

These tend to be numerous and not all of them are relevant. Some are repetitions; some are insignificant, such as an MA from Oxford or Cambridge, which bachelors of those universities purchase two years after graduation, without further examination, for a small fee. This is a short guide to the important ones

BCh or BChir: Bachelor of Surgery, one of the basic qualifications.

BS: Bachelor of Surgery, as above.

DCH: Diploma of Child Health. Awarded in London by the Institute of Child Health, the academic unit of the Hospital for Sick Children, Great Ormond Street. This qualification is taken alike by physicians and surgeons who wish to do paediatric work.

DM: Doctor of Medicine, a degree requiring original research.

DPhil: literally, Doctor of Philosophy – doctorate in medicine, awarded for original research.

FFOphth: a new postgraduate qualification in ophthalmology, awarded by the Faculty of Ophthalmology.

FRCOG: Fellow of the Royal College of Obstetricians and Gynaecologists. Unlike the FRCP, this is awarded almost automatically to MRCOGs after several years of successful practice.

FRCP: Fellow of the Royal College of Physicians. A still higher distinction than MRCP. Until now, it has been awarded selectively – capriciously, some have complained – to physicians who "make a substantial contribution to medicine". A few have received it early in their careers for a prestigious breakthrough; many more as a pre-retirement gong.
  It is likely that in future it will be awarded on completion of two years' satisfactory work, after passing the MRCP exam.

FRCPsych: Fellow of the Royal College of Psychiatrists. Like

FRCOG, *this is awarded almost automatically for several years of satisfactory work after qualifying for membership.*

FRCS: *Fellow of the Royal College of Surgeons. The equivalent in surgery of MRCP, earned by passing a competitive exam designed to identify those who may be fit to become consultant surgeons.*

LRCP and MRCS: *Licentiate of the Royal College of Physicians and Member of the Royal College of Surgeons. Often, a doctor who puts both MB, BS and LRCP, MRCS after his name sat for both exams because his tutor feared he might fail one — they are equivalent basic qualifications.*

MB: *Bachelor of Medicine – one of the basic qualifications required to practise as a doctor.*

MChir: *Master of Surgery. A postgraduate degree, roughly the surgical equivalent of MD, requiring original research.*

MD: *Doctor of Medicine, awarded for original research.*

MRCOG: *Member of the Royal College of Obstetricians and Gynaecologists. This is the essential diploma for seeking to become a consultant obstetrician and/or gynaecologist.*

MRCP: *Member of the Royal College of Physicians. A high diploma, possessed by few GPs, but an essential step towards becoming a consultant physician.*

MRCPsych: *Member of the Royal College of Psychiatrists. The essential qualification to become a consultant psychiatrist. These days, a PhD or MD as well as an MPhil in psychiatry will often be acquired during the struggle to the top. Since the college is of relatively new creation, older psychiatrists have already received an MRCP or even more likely an FRCP.*

MRCS: *Member of the Royal College of Surgeons. A basic qualification – an MRCS has passed half the exams required to become a houseman but not yet a GP. It is the equivalent of LRCP.*

MS: Master of Surgery. A postgraduate degree, roughly the surgical equivalent of MD, requiring original research.

MSc: Master of Science. This degree is often taken by medical students who wish to pursue research for at least a part of their careers.

PhD: Another abbreviation for Doctor of Philosophy – doctorate in medicine, awarded for original research.

Major Fields of Medicine and Surgery

Anaesthesia

This is a far more complex and sophisticated medical skill than merely putting a patient to sleep. The anaesthetist is a highly qualified physician who is responsible for ensuring a patient's survival during and after the operation. A major advance in anaesthetists' skills in recent years has been the development of post-operative intensive care.

Anaesthetists are not named in this book because they are nominated by the surgeon, and a good working relationship between the two is very important.

Cardiology

The medicine of the heart and vascular system. Increasingly, heart conditions that would previously have required surgery, are now treated by cardiologists using invasive techniques such as dilation of coronary arteries by specialised catheterisation.

Chest medicine

The medicine concerned with the trachea, bronchi and lungs. It includes the treatment of asthma (and, by progression, other diseases caused by allergies), bronchitis, emphysema and lung cancer.

Dermatology

The medicine of diseases of the skin. This is more wide-ranging than is generally thought. Many diseases that first show as rashes turn out to be of much greater significance and affect the whole body.

Diabetology

This has only fairly recently evolved as a distinct speciality. Diabetes was previously looked after by endocrinologists or specialists in metabolism, and sometimes still is.

Endocrinology

This is another fairly new speciality, in which most senior

practitioners are academics and accept few private patients. It is the medicine of hormones: the products of the thyroid and the pituitary glands, which circulate in the blood; those of the reproductive organs, which affect fertility; and those working within organs such as the brain or kidney, but affecting the whole body.

ENT (otolaryngology)

This is essentially a surgical speciality treating diseases and disorders of the ears, nose and throat, including the larynx.

Gastroenterology

The medicine of the intestinal tract, which processes food and drink from the oesophagus to the anus. The liver, biliary system and pancreas are also included in this speciality.

General surgery

This is usually a euphemism for abdominal surgery. Abdominal failure is the cause of many emergency operations. 'General surgeons' are also concerned with the gall bladder and with abdominal cancer.

Genito-urinary medicine

The medical treatment of sexually transmitted diseases. The AIDS scare, and thus the increased use of condoms, has resulted in a marked decrease in the incidence of these diseases in Britain.

Haematology

The medicine of diseases and disorders of the blood. It is largely an academic preserve.

Head and neck surgery

A branch of ENT, it deals with those areas of the head and neck other than the brain (which comes under Neurosurgery) and is increasingly aligned with maxillofacial surgery (relating to the face and upper jaw bone).

Heart surgery

It tends still to be transplants that make the headlines, but recent breakthroughs have been more impressive in micro-surgery and repairs to specific parts of the heart.

Medical oncology

Cancer treatment. This branch is mainly concerned with chemotherapy, the efficacy of which has dramatically increased in recent years, with major reductions in its side effects. The value of medical oncology is that it deals with the whole patient.

Nephrology

The medicine of the kidney and urinary tract. Nephrologists, as physicians, work closely with urological surgeons.

Neurology

The medicine of the nervous system, including the brain, and the treatment of diseases of the nervous system such as multi-ple sclerosis and Parkinson's disease.

Neurosurgery

Surgery of the nervous system, including the brain and, increasingly, the spine. Neurosurgeons usually look after head-injury patients. Elective surgery should always be arranged by a neurologist.

Obstetrics and gynaecology

Increasing specialisation makes some doctors in this field con-centrate mostly on obstetrics (pregnancy and childbirth), while others concentrate on gynaecology (the surgical and other treatments of diseases and disorders of the female reproductive and urinary systems). Major recent developments are in the treatment of incontinence and menopause.

Ophthalmology

Eye surgery is increasingly specialised, some surgeons

concentrating on the front of the eye, some on the back of it, including the retina. Some are more concerned with eye problems caused by diabetes, others with glaucoma; some with corneal grafts, others with tumours.

Orthopaedics

The surgery of the bones and joints, increasingly involving the use of spare parts: the artificial hip, knee and, recently, femur.

Paediatrics

Deals with children from birth (or before) up to the age of about twelve. Like adult medicine it is increasingly specialised. There have been particularly dramatic advances in surgery, including prenatal surgery.

Plastic surgery

This is divided into reconstructive and cosmetic surgery. The latter is rarely available on the NHS, except for breast reduction, and the appropriate qualifications for its proper practice in the private sector is the subject of fierce dispute. Plastic surgeons also surgically treat burns.

Psychiatry

Most psychiatrists use drugs and various forms of psycho-therapy. Their particular challenges are to find more effective treatments for schizophrenia and acute depression – or even to agree whether they are manifestations of the same disease or different ones. Meanwhile many concentrate on marital and sexual problems, and those of addiction.

Radiotherapy

The use of ionising radiation to attack cancerous cells.

Rheumatology

The non-surgical treatment of diseases of the joints and the pain they cause. It includes the use of drugs and techniques of rehabilitation.

Thoracic surgery

Surgery of the chest. With the change to non-surgical treatment of tuberculosis, it became a sideline of heart surgeons. Recent advances in minimally invasive techniques have led to some striking advances, including in the removal of tumours. A field to watch.

Urology

Medicine of the urinary and genital organs (including the prostate) and the kidneys. Recent developments include non-surgical and minimally-invasive treatments of prostate problems.

Vascular surgery

The surgery of the blood vessels. This may now involve microsurgery to reconstruct injured tissue and blood vessels. It is still largely an academic preserve.

Virology

Another mostly academic branch of medicine, which has yet to develop much in the way of effective clinical treatments.

Seventy Outstanding Specialists Outside London

This list was compiled in the spring of 1993, at the request of the *People* newspaper, to show that specialist medicine of an international standard is practised outside London, in NHS hospitals.

Allergists

Dr David Pearson, FRCP.
Withington Hospital, Nell Lane, West Didsbury, Manchester M20 8LR. Tel: 061 445 8111. Immunisation against allergies.

Professor John Warner, MD, FRCP.
University Child Health, Southampton General Hospital, Level G, Centre Block, Southampton, SO9 4XY. Tel: 0703 796160. Britain's Children's food and other allergies.

Alzheimer's disease

Dr Robert Hunter, MRCPsych.
Gartnavel Royal Hospital, 1055 Great Western Road, Glasgow G12 0XH. Tel: 041 334 6241. Alzheimer's disease and dementia.

Cancer specialists

Dr Eric Bessell, PhD, MRCP, FRCR.
Nottingham University Hospital, Park Row, Nottingham, NG1 6HA. Tel: 0602 481100. Radiotherapy.

Professor Adrian Harris, DPHIL, FRCP,
ICRF Clinical Oncology Unit, Churchill Hospital, Headington, Oxford OX3 7LJ. Tel: 0865 741841. First-class medicine and a caring approach.

Dr Robin Hunter, FRCP.
Christie Hospital NHS Trust, Wilmslow Road, Withington, Manchester M20 9BX. Tel: 061 446 3000. Runs Britain's biggest cancer hospital. Top-quality treatment in spartan premises.

Professor David Johnston, MD, FRCS.
Leeds General Infirmary, Gt George Street, Leeds LS1 3EN.
Tel: 0532 432799. Bringing survival rates for gastric cancer up
from Britain's 10 per cent to Japan's 50 per cent.

Professor Stan Kaye, MD, FRCP.
Beatson Oncology Centre, Western Infirmary, Glasgow G11
6NT. Tel: 041 339 8822. Innovations in chemotherapy.

Professor Sidney Lowry, FRCPI, FRCR.
Northern Ireland Oncology Centre, Belvoir Park Hospital,
Hospital Road, Belfast BT8 8JR. Tel: 0232 491942. Top
medical quality in friendly atmosphere. Authority on radiation
sickness.

Dr Malcolm Mcillmurray, DM, FRCP.
Royal Lancaster Infirmary, Ashton Road, Lancaster LA1 4RT.
Tel: 0524 65944. Runs the NHS's leading holistic centre for
treating people with cancer.

Professor Peter Selby MD, MRCP.
St James Hospital, Beckett Street, Leeds LS9 7TS. Tel: 0532
433144. Emphasises quality of life. One of the few cancer
doctors in the world to rival Tokyo in treating gastric cancer.

Cardiologists

Dr Steve Forfar, MD, FRCP.
John Radcliffe Hospital, Headley Way, Headington, Oxford
OX3 9DU. Tel: 0865 741166. Authority on hormonal aspects
and drug treatments of heart disease.

Dr Leslie Hamilton, MD, FRCP.
Freeman Hospital, Freeman Road, High Heaton, Newcastle-
upon-Tyne NE7 7DN. Tel: 091 284 3111. Supervision of
children's heart transplants.

Dr Michael Petch, MD, FRCP.
Papworth Hospital, Papworth Everard, Cambridge CB3 8RE.
Tel: 0480 830541. Outstanding generalist.

Dr Kent Woods, MD, MRCP.
Leicester Royal Infirmary NHS Trust, Leicester LE1 5WW.
Tel: 0533 541414. Hormonal aspects of heart disease.

Chest physicians

Dr Peter Davies, DM, MRCP.
Cardio-Thoracic Centre, Thomas Drive, Liverpool LI4 3PE.
Tel: 051 228 1616. Prominent in the new war against
resurging tuberculosis.

Dr Jimmy Paten, MD, MRCP.
Royal Hospital for Sick Children, Yorkhill, Glasgow.
Tel: 041 339 8888. Breathing difficulties in children.

Childbirth specialists

Dr Cambell Davidson, FRCP.
Alderhay Children's Hospital, Eton Road, Merseyside L12
2AP. Tel: 051 228 4811. Hospital professor.

Dr Kiernan Fitzpatrick, FFA, FRCSI.
Belfast City Hospital, Lisburn Road, Belfast BT9 7AB.
Tel: 0232 329241. Pain management during pregnancy.

Malcolm Levene, MD, FRCP.
Clarendon Wing, General Infirmary, Leeds. Tel: 0532 432799.
Diagnosis and treatment of brain damage in unborn children.

Dr Colin Morley, MD, FRCP.
Addenbrooke's Hospital, Hills Road, Cambridge CB2 2QQ.
Tel: 0223 245151. Babies' breathing problems – avoidance of
cot deaths.

Professor Edwin Symonds, MD, FRCOG.
Nottingham University Hospital, Queen's Medical Centre,
Derby Road, Nottingham NT7 2UH. Tel: 0602 421421.
Complications in pregnancy, including hypertension in mother
and child.

Professor Martin Whittle, MD, FRCP, FRCOG.
Birmingham Maternity Hospital, Queen Elizabeth Medical
Centre, Metchley Park Road, Edgbaston, Birmingham B15
2TG. Tel: 021 472 1377. Pregnancies outside as well as inside
the womb.

Child and Adolescent psychiatrist

Dr Michael Shooter, FRCPsych.
Preswylfa Child and Family Centre, Canton, Cardiff. Tel:
0222 3444 89.

Crohn's disease specialists

Dr Robert Allan, PhD, MD, FRCP.
Gastroenterological Unit, General Hospital, Steel House Lane,
Birmingham B4 6NH. Tel: 021 236 8611.

Professor John Rhodes, MD, FRCP.
University Hospital of Wales, Heath Park, Cardiff CF4 4XW.
Tel: 0222 747747. Identified a form of bowel cancer associat-
ed with nicotine deprivation.

Dermatologists

Dr William Cunliffe, MD, FRCP.
Leeds General Infirmary, Gt George Street, Leeds LS1 3EN.
Tel: 0532 316446. Baldness in women.

Dr Dafydd Roberts, MRCP.
Singleton Hospital, Swansea SA2 8QA. Tel: 0792 205666.
Acne in adolescents.

Diabetologists

Professor Kurt Alberti, MD, FRCPATH, FRCP.
Department of Medicine, Framlington Place, Newcastle-upon-
Tyne NE1 4LP. Tel: 091 232 5131.

Dr Adrian Barnes, MD, FRCP.
Barnet General Hospital, Wellhouse Lane, Barnet,
Herts EN5 3DJ. Tel: 081 440 5111.

Ear, Nose and Throat specialists

Professor George Browning, MD, FRCS.
Royal Infirmary, 82-84 Castle Street, Glasgow G4 0SF. Tel:
041 552 3535. Ear surgery.

Mr Norman Haacke, FRCS.
Southampton University Hospital, Southampton SO9 4XY.
Tel: 0703 796 741. Implants for profoundly deaf children.

Epilepsy specialists

Dr Richard Appleton, MRCP.
Child Development Centre, Alderhay Children's Hospital,
Liverpool LP12 2AP. Tel: 051 228 4811.

Dr John Stephenson, FRCP.
Royal Hospital for Sick Children, York Hill, Glasgow G3 8SG.
Tel: 041 339 8888.

Gynaecologists

Professor John Newton, MD, FRCOG.
Birmingham Maternity Hospital, Edgbaston, Birmingham B15
2TG. Tel: 021 472 1377. Redesigning the IUD to emit hormones to end heavy periods.

Heart surgeon

Professor Keith Fox, FRCS, FRCP.
Royal Infirmary, 1 Lauriston Place, Edinburgh EH3 9YW.
Tel: 031 229 2477. Cardiomyoplasty pioneer, transplanting
muscle from patient's own body instead of a complete heart
from another.

Hernia surgeon

Mr Andrew Kingsnorth, FRCS.
Royal Liverpool University Hospital, Prescot Street, Liverpool
L7 8XP. Tel: 051 706 2000. Introduced safer, more durable
technique from France.

HIV/AIDS physician

Dr Raymond Brettle, FRCP.
Infectious Diseases Unit, City Hospital, 51 Greenbank Drive, Edinburgh EH10 5SB. Tel: 031 447 1001. Top practitioner in the field.

Infertility specialists

Mr Michael Booker, FRCOG.
Mayday Hospital, Croydon CR7 7YE. Tel: 081 684 6999. Brought Liverpool University's Transport in vitro fertilisation breakthrough to southern district general hospital.

Professor Michael Hull, MD, FRCOG.
Bristol Maternity Hospital, St Michael's Hill, Bristol. Tel: 0272 215 411. Multi-disciplinary and innovative.

Mr Charles Kingsland, FRCOG.
Royal Liverpool Hospital, Prescott Street, Liverpool L7 8XP. Tel: 051 706 2000. In vitre fertilisation and male infertility.

Kidney specialists

Professor Netar Mallick, FRCP.
Manchester Royal Infirmary, Oxford Rd, Manchester M0J H13. Tel: 061 276 1234. Brought in by the government to sort out kidney medicine in London.

Mr Murray Ross-Taylor, FRCS.
Royal Victoria Infirmary, Queen Victoria Road, Newcastle-upon-Tyne NE1 4LP. Tel: 091 232 5131. Transplant surgeon in an exemplary NHS unit.

Liver surgeons

Sir Roy Calne, FRS, FRCS.
Addenbrooke's Hospital, Hill Road, Cambridge CB2 2QQ. Tel: 0223 245151. One of the great surgical pioneers of the century.

Mr Michael Thick, FRCS.
Royal Victoria Infirmary, Newcastle-upon-Tyne NE1 4LP.
Tel: 091 232 5131.

Neurologists and Neuro surgeons

Mr Thomas Hide, FRCS.
Institute of Neurological Sciences, Southern General Hospital,
1345 Govan Road, Glasgow G51 4TF. Tel: 041 445 2466.
Cases are referred to him from all over the UK.

Prof A David Mendelow, FRCS.
Newcastle General Hospital, Westgate Road, Newcastle-upon-
Tyne NE4 6BE. Tel: 091 273 8811. New microsurgery
techniques for brain and spine.

Mr David R. Sandeman, FRCS.
Frenchay Hospital, Bristol BS16 1LE. Tel: 0272 701212.
Leader in new techniques of fine-target surgery.

Old People's medicine

Dr Andrew Fairbairn, MRCPsych.
St Nicholas Hospital, Newcastle-upon-Tyne. NE3 3T
Tel: 091 213 0151. Mental problems of old age.

Dr Richard Shepherd, FRCP.
Consultant Geriatrician, Leicester General Hospital,
Gwendolen Road, Leicester, LE5 4PW. Tel: 0533 490490.
Management of Parkinson's disease.

Dr Stephen Webster, MD, FRCP.
Adenbrooke's Hospital, Hills Road, Cambridge. CB2 2QQ.
Tel: 0223 245151. Techniques of avoiding senility.

Opthalmologists

Professor David Easty, MD, FRCS.
Bristol Eye Hospital, Lower Maudlin Street, Bristol BS1 2LX.
Tel: 0272 230060. Pioneering new corneal treatment.

Professor David McLeod FRCS.
Manchester Royal Eye Hospital, Oxford Road, Manchester
M13 9WH. Tel: 061 276 5620. Star of retinal laser surgery.

Orthopaedic surgeons

Mr Christopher Colton, FRCS.
Nottingham University Hospital, Derby Road, Nottingham
NT7 2UH. Tel: 0602 421421. Elbows and upper arm. Chosen
to operate on Prince Charles. Also expert with children.

Mr David Dandy, FRCS.
Addenbrooke's Hospital, Hills Road, Cambridge CB2 2QQ.
Tel: 0223 245151. The international lecturer and practitioner
of knee surgery to whom Mr Christopher Coltron referred
Prince Charles.

Mr Peter Edmond, CBE, FRCS.
National Spinal Injuries Unit, 1345 Govan Road, Southern
General Hospital, Glasgow G51 4TF. Tel: 041 445 2466.

Mr Raymond Ross, FRCS.
Hope Hospital, Eckles Old Road, Salford, Manchester M6
8HD. Tel: 061 789 7373. Spinal disc implants.

Paediatrician

(See also under different specialities.)
Professor David Hull, FRCP.
Department of Child Health, Queen's Medical Centre,
University Hospital, Nottingham NT7 2UH. Tel: 0602
421421.

Plastic micro-surgeons

Ms Ann Brain, FRCS.
Withington Hospital, Manchester M20 8LR. Tel: 061 445
8111. Rejoins severed limbs in surgical marathons.

Mr Neil McLean, FRCS.
Newcastle General Hospital, Westgate, Newcastle-upon-Tyne
NE4 6BE. Tel: 091 273 8811.

Mr Philip Sykes, FRCS.
St Lawrence Hospital, Chepstow, Gwent, Wales NT6 5YX.
Tel: 0291 622 334. Top hand surgeon in star NHS plastic
microsurgery unit.

Rheumatologists

Professor Paul Dieppe, FRCP.
Bristol Royal Infirmary, Maudlin Street, Bristol BS2 8HW.
Tel: 0272 230 000. Osteoporosis of the knee. Pioneer of
techniques to free many sufferers from pain and getting them
mobile, without drugs.

Dr Roger Francis, MRCP.
Newcastle General Hospital, Westgate Road, Newcastle-upon-
Tyne NE4 6BE. Tel: 091 273 8811. Osteoporosis in men – a
condition that is far more common than previously realised.

Professor Roger Shurrock, FRCP.
Victoria Infirmary, Grange Road, Lineside, Glasgow G42
9TY. Tel: 041 649 4545. Arthritis.

Dr Anthony Ward, MRCP.
Haywood Hospital, Stoke-on-Trent, Staffordshire ST6 7AG.
Tel: 0782 835721. Sports injuries.

Snoring specialist

Dr John Shneerson, MD, FRCP.
Papworth Hospital, Papworth Everard, Cambridge CB3 8RE.
Tel: 0480 830541. Snoring cured through five-minutes laser
treatment.

Trauma specialists

Mr Peter C Bewes, FRCS.
Senior Consultant, Birmingham City Accident Hospital, Bath
Row, Ladywood, Birmingham B15 1NA. Tel: 021 627 1627.
Even London trauma specialists say that if you're going to have
a serious accident, Birmingham is the best place to have it.

Dr Peter J. Eames, MSc, MRCP, MRCPsych.
Medical Director, Grafton Manor, Towcester, Northants
NN12 7SS. Tel: 0908 543 131. Best unit in Britain for rehabil-
itation after severe head injury. Consultant to the Royal Air
Force. Takes NHS health-authority referrals.

Dr James R. Scott, FRCPsych.
Belfast City Hospital, Lisburn Road, Belfast BT9 7AB. Tel:
0232 329241. Psychological trauma.

The List

AMYLOIDOSIS PHYSICIAN

PEPYS, Professor Mark B.

PRIVATE: Refer to address and number below.
NHS AND ACADEMIC: Professor of Immunological Medicine,
Royal Postgraduate Medical School, Hammersmith Hospital,
Du Cane Road, London W12 0NN.
Tel: 081 740 3202. Fax: 081 749 7478.

MAJOR DEGREES: *PhD, MD, MRCPath, FRCP. First qualified
in Cambridge in 1968. Specialist training in Cambridge, and at
the Royal Free Hospital, London.*

ARTERIAL AND VASCULAR SURGEONS

BASKERVILLE, Mr Paul A.

PRIVATE: 147 Harley Street, London W1N 1DJ.
Tel: 071 224 3254.
NHS : Consultant Surgeon, King's College Hospital,
Denmark Hill, London SE5 9RS. Tel: 071 274 6222.

MAJOR DEGREES: *DM, FRCS. First qualified in Oxford in 1974.*
Specialist training at St Bartholomew's and St Thomas's hospi-
tals, London.

BISHOP, Mr Christopher C. R.

PRIVATE: Refer to address and number below.
NHS : Consultant Surgeon, Whittington Hospital,
Highgate Hill, London N19 5NF. Tel: 071 272 3070.

MAJOR DEGREE: *FRCS. First qualified in Cambridge in 1978.*
Specialist training at St Thomas's Hospital, London.

CROFT, Mr Rodney J.

PRIVATE: 144 Harley Street, London W1N 1AH.
Tel: 071 935 0023.
NHS : Consultant General and Vascular Surgeon,
North Middlesex Hospital, Sterling Road, Edmonton,
London N18 1QX. Tel: 081 807 3071.

ACADEMIC: *Clinical Sub-Dean, Royal Free Hospital Medical*
School. MAJOR DEGREES: *FRCS, FACS, MChir. First qualified*
in Cambridge in 1969. Specialist training at the Middlesex and
Central Middlesex hospitals. USA: Fellow, American College
of Surgeons.

in Wantage?

GREENHALGH, Professor Roger M.

PRIVATE: Refer to address and number below.
NHS AND ACADEMIC: Professor of Surgery, Charing Cross
Hospital, Fulham Palace Road, London SW10 9NH.
Tel: 081 846 7316. Fax: 081 846 7330.

MAJOR DEGREES: MD, FRCS. DISTINCTIONS: Councillor,
Association of Surgeons. Specialist training at St
Bartholomew's and Charing Cross hospitals, London. First
qualified in Cambridge in 1967. USA: Visiting Professor,
Harvard; Baylor College of Medicine, Dallas.

HOBBS, Mr John T.

PRIVATE: 4 Upper Wimpole Street, London W1M 7TD.
Tel: 071 323 2830.
NHS : Consultant Surgeon, St Mary's Hospital, Praed Street,
London W2 1NY. Tel: 071 725 6666. Fax: 071 725 6200.

ACADEMIC: Senior Lecturer, St Mary's and St George's
Hospitals. MAJOR DEGREES: MD, FRCS. First qualified in
London in 1954. Specialist training in Birmingham and at
St Mary's Hospital. USA: Lately Research Fellow in Surgery,
Harvard Medical School.

MANSFIELD, Miss Averil O.

PRIVATE: 66 Harley Street, London W1N 1AE.
Tel: 071 323 4714.
NHS : Consultant Surgeon, St Mary's Hospital, Praed Street,
London W2 INY. Tel: 071 725 6666. Fax: 071 725 6200

ACADEMIC: Director of Postgraduate Studies, St Mary's, Senior

Lecturer in Vascular Surgery, Royal Postgraduate Medical School. DISTINCTION: *Chairman, Court of Examiners, Royal College of Surgeons. Major degrees: Mch, FRCS. First qualified in Liverpool in 1960. Specialist training at the Royal Liverpool Hospital.*

NICOLAIDES, Professor Andreas N.

Especially non-invasive cardiovascular investigations.
PRIVATE: Refer to address and number below.
NHS AND ACADEMIC: Professor of Vascular Surgery,
St Mary's Hospital, Praed Street, London W2 1NY.
Tel: 071 262 1280 or 725 6666. Fax: 071 725 6200.

DISTINCTION: *Jacksonian Prize, Royal College of Surgeons.*
MAJOR DEGREES: *MS, FRCS. First qualified in London in 1962. Specialist training at King's College Hospital.*

SCURR, Mr John H.

PRIVATE: 5 Balniel Gate, London SW1V 3SD.
Tel: 071 834 5578. Fax: 071 834 6315.
NHS AND ACADEMIC: Senior Lecturer and Honorary
Consultant, Middlesex Hospital, Mortimer Street,
London W1N 8AA. Tel: 071 636 8333. Fax: 071 323 0397.

MAJOR DEGREE: *FRCS. First qualified (with honours) in London in 1969. Specialist training at the Westminster and Middlesex Hospitals.*

WOLFE, Mr John H. N.

PRIVATE: 66 Harley Street, London W1N 1AE.
Tel: 071 580 5030. Fax: 071 631 5341.
NHS: Consultant Surgeon, St Mary's Hospital,
Praed Street, London W2 1NY.
Tel: 071 262 1280 or 725 6666. Fax: 071 725 6200.

ACADEMIC: *Senior Lecturer, Royal Postgraduate Medical School.* DISTINCTION: *Lately Hunterian Professor, Royal College of Surgeons.* MAJOR DEGREES: *MS, FRCS. First qualified in London in 1981. Specialist training at St Thomas's Hospital.* USA: *Lately Research Fellow, Harvard University.*

CARDIOLOGISTS

BALCON, Dr Raphael.

PRIVATE: 22 Upper Wimpole Street, London WIM 7TA.
Tel: 071 486 8691 Fax: 071 486 7918.
NHS: Consultant Cardiologist, London Chest Hospital,
Bonner Road, London E2 9JX.
Tel: 081 980 4433. Fax: 081 983 2278.

ACADEMIC: *Senior Lecturer, Cardiothoracic Institute.*
Distinction: Councillor, British Cardiac Society. MAJOR
DEGREES: *MD, FRCP. First qualified in London in 1960.*
Specialist training at King's College and the National Heart
hospitals. USA: Lately Fellow in Cardiology, Wayne State
University, Detroit.

BANIM, Dr Seamus.

PRIVATE: 62 Wimpole Street, London W1M 7DE.
Tel: 071 486 1813.
NHS : Consultant Cardiologist, St Bartholomew's Hospital,
West Smithfield, London EC1A 7BE.
Tel: 071 601 8888. Fax: 071 601 7899.

MAJOR DEGREE: *FRCP. First qualified in Oxford in 1967.*
Specialist training at the Royal Postgraduate Medical School
and the Royal Brompton and National Heart Hospital.

CAMM, Professor Alan J.

Electrophysiology.
PRIVATE: Refer to address and number below.
NHS AND ACADEMIC: Professor of Clinical Cardiology,
St George's Hospital, Blackshaw Road, London SW17 0QT.
Tel: 081 672 1255.

MAJOR DEGREES: MD, FRCP. First qualified in London in 1971. Specialist training at St Batholomew's. Previously Professor of Cardiovascular Medicine, St Bartholomew's Hospital. USA: Fellow, American College of Cardiologists.

COLTART, Dr John.

PRIVATE: 47 Weymouth Street, London W1N 3LD.
Tel: 071 486 5787.
NHS: Consultant Cardiologist, St Thomas's Hospital, Lambeth Palace Road, London SE1 7EH.
Tel: 071 928 9292. Fax: 071 922 8079.

MAJOR DEGREES: MD, FRCP. First qualified in London in 1967. Specialist training at St Bartholomew's Hospital and the Royal Postgraduate Medical School. USA: Lately Fellow in Cardiology, Stanford University, California.

CURRY, Dr Paul V. L.

PRIVATE: Emblem House, London Bridge Hospital, 27 Tooley Street, London SE1 2PR.
Tel: 071 403 0824. Fax: 071 407 3162.
NHS: Consultant Cardiologist, Guy's Hospital, St Thomas Street, London SE1 9RT. Tel: 071 955 5000.

DISTINCTION: Goulstonian Lecturer, Royal College of Physicians. MAJOR DEGREES: MD, FRCP. First qualified (with honours) in London in 1969. Specialist training at the Royal Brompton and National Heart Hospital and the Royal Postgraduate Medical School.

FOX, Dr Kim M.

Electrocardiography.
PRIVATE: 34 Devonshire Place, London W1N 1PE.
Tel: 071 486 4617.
NHS: Consultant in Charge, Department of
Electrocardiography, Royal Brompton National Heart and
Lung Hospital, Fulham Road, London SW3 6HP.
Tel: 071 352 8121. Fax: 071 351 8099.

*MAJOR DEGREES: MD, FRCP. First qualified in St Andrews
in 1971. Specialist training at the Royal Postgraduate
Medical School.*

JEWITT, Dr David E.

Private: Refer to address and number below.
Tel: 071 274 8570.
NHS: Director, Cardiac Unit, King's College Hospital,
Denmark Hill, London SE5 9RS.
Tel: 071 274 6222. Fax: 071 326 3589.

*ACADEMIC: Lately Consultant Cardiac Physician and Senior
Lecturer, Royal Postgraduate Medical School. MAJOR DEGREE:
FRCP. First qualified (with honours and university medal) in
London in 1962. Specialist training at King's College Hospital
and the Royal Postgraduate Medical School.*

McDONALD, Dr Alastair H.

PRIVATE: Refer to address and number below.
NHS: Consultant Cardiologist, Royal London Hospital,
Whitechapel Road, London E1 1BB.
Tel: 071 377 7000. Fax: 071 377 7396 or 7122.

ACADEMIC: Senior Lecturer in Cardiology, London Hospital.

MAJOR DEGREE: FRCP. *First qualified in Edinburgh in 1962. Specialist training in Edinburgh and at the National Heart Hospital and the Royal London Hospital.*

NATHAN, Dr Anthony.

Abnormal heart rhythms, including in children.
PRIVATE: BUPA Hospital, Heathbourne Road, Bushey, Herts WD2 1RD. Tel: 081 420 4471.
NHS: Consultant Cardiologist, St Bartholomew's Hospital, West Smithfield, London EC1A 7BE.
Tel: 071 601 8708. Fax: 071 601 7899.

DISTINCTION: *Founding Fellow, European Society of Cardiologists.* MAJOR DEGREES: *MD, FRCP. First qualified in London in 1975. Specialist training at the Royal Brompton and St Bartholomew's hospitals.*

OAKLEY, Dr Celia M.

Congenital heart diseases.
PRIVATE: 23 Harley Street, London W1N 1DA.
Tel: 071 580 4073.
NHS: Consultant Cardiologist, Hammersmith Hospital, 150 Du Cane Road, London W12 0HS.
Tel: 081 743 2030. Fax: 081 740 3169.

ACADEMIC: *Senior Lecturer, Royal Postgraduate Medical School.* MAJOR DEGREES: *MD, FRCP. First qualified (with honours) in London in 1954. Specialist training at the National Heart Hospital and the Royal Postgraduate Medical School.* USA: *Fellow, American College of Cardiologists.*

OLDERSHAW, Dr Paul J.

Echocardiography.
PRIVATE: Private Consulting Rooms, Royal Brompton National
Heart and Lung Hospital, 11 Foulis Terrace,
London SW7 3LZ. Tel: 071 352 6468.
NHS: Consultant Cardiologist, Royal Brompton National
Heart and Lung Hospital, Fulham Road, London SW3 6HP.
Tel: 071 352 8121. Fax: 071 351 8099.

MAJOR DEGREE: FRCP. First qualified in Cambridge in 1974.
Specialist training at St George's and the Royal Brompton and
National Heart Hospitals.

POOLE-WILSON, Professor Philip.

Especially invasive cardiology.
PRIVATE: Refer to address and number below.
NHS AND ACADEMIC: Professor of Cardiology,
Royal Brompton National Heart and Lung Hospital,
Fulham Road, London SW3 6HP.
Tel: 071 352 8121. Fax: 071 351 8099.

MAJOR DEGREES: MD, FRCP. First qualified in 1969 in
Cambridge. Specialist training at St Thomas's, the
Royal Brompton and National Heart Hospital and the
Royal Postgraduate Medical School.

RICKARDS, Dr Anthony F.

Investigative testing, catheters and angiography.
PRIVATE: London Heart Clinic, 22 Upper Wimpole Street,
London W1M 7TA. Tel: 071 486 8961.
NHS: Consultant Cardiologist, Royal Brompton National
Heart and Lung Hospital, Fulham Road, London SW3 6HP.
Tel: 071 352 8121. Fax: 071 351 8099.

ACADEMIC: Lately Vice Dean, Cardiothoracic Institute. Distinction: Lately Secretary, British Cardiac Society. MAJOR DEGREE: FRCP. First qualified in London in 1968. Specialist training at the Middlesex and National Heart Hospitals. USA: Fellow, American College of Cardiologists.

SEVER, Professor Peter S.

Hypertension.
PRIVATE: Refer to address and number below.
NHS: Director, Hypertension Clinic, St Mary's Hospital, Praed Street, London W2 1NY.
Tel: 071 262 1280 or 725 6666. Fax: 071 725 6200.

ACADEMIC: Professor of Clinical Pharmacology and Therapy, St Mary's Hospital Medical School. DISTINCTION: President, British Hypertension Society. MAJOR DEGREE: FRCP. First qualified in Cambridge in 1968. Specialist training at St Mary's Hospital.

SHINEBOURNE, Dr Elliot A.

Heart disorders in children.
PRIVATE: Private Consulting Rooms, Royal Brompton National Heart and Lung Hospital, Foulis Terrace, London SW7 3LZ. Tel: 071 352 6468.
NHS: Consultant Paediatric Cardiologist, Royal Brompton National Heart and Lung Hospital, Fulham Road, London SW3 6HP. Tel: 071 352 8121. Fax: 071 351 8099.

ACADEMIC: Senior Lecturer, Heart and Lung Institute. MAJOR DEGREES: MD, FRCP. First qualified in London in 1970. Specialist training at St Bartholomew's and the National Heart Hospitals. USA: Lately American Heart Association Travelling Fellow in Cardiovascular Medicine.

SOMERVILLE, Dr Jane.

Heart disorders in children.
PRIVATE: 30 York House, Upper Montagu Street,
London W1H 1FR. Tel: 071 723 9146.
NHS: Royal Brompton National Heart and Lung Hospital,
Fulham Road, London SW3 6HP.
Tel: 071 352 8121. Fax: 071 351 8099.

ACADEMIC: *Senior Lecturer, Cardiothoracic Institute and
Lecturer in Paediatric Cardiology, University of Turin, Italy.
MAJOR DEGREES: MD, FRCP. First qualified in London in
1955. Specialist training at the National Heart Hospital.
USA: Fellow, American College of Cardiologists.*

SOWTON, Dr Edgar.

Especially angioplasty.
Private: 25 Upper Wimpole Street, London W1M 7TA.
Tel: 071 935 5625.
NHS: Director of Cardiology, Guy's Hospital, St Thomas
Street, London SE1 9RT. Tel: 071 407 7600.

ACADEMIC: *Lately Reader in Cardiology, University of
London. Distinctions: Raymond Horton-Smith Prize,
Cambridge; Councillor, British Cardiac Society and European
Society of Cardiology. MAJOR DEGREES: MD, FRCP. First qual-
ified in Cambridge in 1957. Specialist training at
St George's and the National Heart Hospitals.
USA: Fellow, American College of Cardiologists.*

SPURRELL, Dr Roworth A. J.

Cardiac catheterisation and angioplasty.
Private: 10 Upper Wimpole Street, London W1M 7TD.
Tel: 071 935 3922.

NHS: Consultant in Charge of Cardiology,
St Bartholomew's Hospital, West Smithfield,
London EC1A 7BE. Tel: 071 601 8888. Fax: 071 601 7899.

MAJOR DEGREES: *MD, FRCP. First qualified in London in
1960. Specialist training at Guy's, St George's and the
National Heart Hospitals, London. USA: Fellow, American
College of Cardiologists.*

SUTTON, Dr Richard.

Especially pacing.
PRIVATE: 149 Harley Street, London W1N 1HG.
Tel: 071 935 4444. Fax: 071 935 6718.
NHS : Consultant Cardiologist, Chelsea and Westminster
Hospital, 369 Fulham Road, London SW10 9NH.
Tel: 081 746 8000. Fax: 081 746 8111.

DISTINCTION: *President, British Pacing Electrophysiology
Group.* MAJOR DEGREE: *DSc, FRCP. First qualified in London
in 1964. Specialist training at the National Heart Hospital.
USA: Lately Research Fellow in Cardiology, University of
North Carolina. Twice awarded the Governors' Award of the
American College of Cardiologists.*

SWANTON, Dr R. Howard.

Angioplasty.
PRIVATE: 25 Upper Wimpole Street, London WIM 7TA.
Tel: 071 935 8805.
NHS: Consultant Cardiologist, Middlesex Hospital,
Mortimer Street, London WIN 8AA. Tel: 071 636 8333.
Fax: 071 323 0397.

MAJOR DEGREES: *MD, FRCP. First qualified in Cambridge in
1970. Specialist training at St Thomas's and the National
Heart Hospitals.*

WEBB-PEPLOE, Dr Michael M.

PRIVATE: York House, 199 Westminster Bridge Road,
London SE1 7UT. Tel: 071 928 5485. Fax: 071 928 3748.
NHS: Consultant in Charge, Department of Cardiology,
St Thomas's Hospital, Lambeth Palace Road,
London SE1 7EH. Tel: 071 928 9292 Fax: 071 922 8079.

*DISTINCTION: Consultant in Cardiology to the Army. MAJOR
DEGREE: FRCP. First qualified in Cambridge in 1961.
Specialist training at the Royal Brompton and National Heart
Hospital and the Royal Postgraduate Medical School.*

CHEST PHYSICIANS

BARNES, Professor Peter

PRIVATE: Private Consulting Rooms, Royal Brompton National Heart and Lung Hospital, 11 Foulis Terrace, London SW7 3LZ. Tel: 071 352 6468.
NHS: Consultant Physician, Royal Brompton National Heart and Lung Hospital, Fulham Road, London SW3 6HP.
Tel: 071 352 8121. Fax: 071 351 8099.

ACADEMIC: Professor, National Heart and Lung Institute.
MAJOR DEGREE: FRCP. First qualified in Oxford in 1972.
Specialist training at the Royal Postgraduate Medical School.

BATEMAN, Dr Nigel T.

PRIVATE: York House, 199 Westminster Bridge Road, London SEI 7UT. Tel: 071 928 5485. Fax: 071 928 3748.
NHS: Consultant Physician, St Thomas's Hospital, Lambeth Palace Road, London SEI 7EH.
Tel: 071 928 9292. Fax: 071 922 8079.

MAJOR DEGREE: FRCP. First qualified in Oxford in 1969.

CLARKE, Dr Stewart W.

PRIVATE: 148 Harley Street, London W1N 1AH.
Tel: 071 487 5020.
NHS: Consultant Physician, Royal Free Hospital, Pond Street, London NW3 2QG. Tel: 071 794 0500. Fax: 071 4335 5342.

ACADEMIC: Lately Lecturer, Queen Elizabeth Hospital, Birmingham. DISTINCTION: Member, Association of Physicians. MAJOR DEGREES: MD, FRCP (with honours). First qualified in Birmingham in 1959. Specialist training at the Royal Brompton and National Heart Hospital. USA: Lately Senior Fellow, University of California Medical Center, San Francisco.

COLLINS, Dr John V.

PRIVATE: 28 Weymouth Street, London W1N 3FA.
Tel: 071 487 5550.
NHS: Consultant Physician, Royal Brompton National Heart
and Lung Hospital, Fulham Road, London SW3 6HP.
Tel: 071 352 8121. Fax: 071 351 8099.

DISTINCTION: *Consultant Physician, Royal Hospital, Chelsea.*
MAJOR DEGREES: FRCP, MD. First qualified in London in
1966. Specialist training at St Bartholomew's and the Royal
Brompton and National Heart Hospitals.

COSTELLO, Dr John.

PRIVATE: 59 Harley Street, London W1N 1DD.
Tel: 071 580 8704.
NHS: Director, Chest Unit, King's College Hospital,
Denmark Hill, London SE5 9RS.
Tel: 071 274 6222. Fax: 071 326 3589.

ACADEMIC: *Senior Lecturer, King's College Hospital. MAJOR*
DEGREE: FRCP. First qualified in Dublin in 1968. Specialist
training at the Royal Infirmary, Edinburgh, and the Royal
Brompton and National Heart Hospital. USA: Lately
Assistant Professor in Medicine, University of California.

DAVIES, Professor Robert J.

Especially allergies.
PRIVATE: Refer to address and number below.
NHS: Consultant Physician, Respiratory Medicine, St
Bartholomew's Hospital, West Smithfield, London EC1A 7BE.
Tel: 071 601 8436 or 8438. Fax: 071 601 7899.

ACADEMIC: *Professor of Respiratory Medicine, St*
Bartholomew's. DISTINCTIONS: President of the British and

Executive of the International Association of Allergology and Clinical Immunology; Editor, Journal of Respiratory Medicine; *author;* Allergy: The Facts. MAJOR DEGREES: *MD, FRCP. First qualified in Cambridge 1968. Specialist training at St Thomas's and the Royal Brompton and National Heart Hospitals. USA: Lately Medical Fellow, Tulane University, New Orleans; Fellow, American Academy of Allergy and Immunology.*

EMPEY, Dr Duncan W.

PRIVATE: 45 Wimpole Street, London W1M 7DG.
Tel: 071 935 2977. Fax: 071 935 2740.
NHS: Consultant Physician, Royal London Hospital, Whitechapel, London E1 1BB. Tel: 071 377 7000.
Fax: 071 377 7396 or 7122.

DISTINCTIONS: *Editor,* British Journal of Diseases of the Chest. *Executive Committee, European Society of Clinical Respiratory Physiology.*MAJOR DEGREE: *FRCP. First qualified in London in 1969. Specialist training at the Royal London and the Royal Brompton and National Heart Hospitals. USA: Lately Fellow, Cardiovascular Research Institute, University of California, San Francisco.*

EVANS, Dr Timothy W.

PRIVATE: Refer to address and number below.
NHS AND ACADEMIC: Consultant Physician and Senior Lecturer, Royal Brompton National Heart and Lung Hospital, Fulham Road, London SW2 6HP.
Tel: 071 352 8121. Fax: 071 351 8473.

DISTINCTION: *Lately Doverdale Fellow, Royal Brompton National Heart Hospital.* MAJOR DEGREE: *MRCP. First qualified in Oxford in 1979. Specialist training at the Royal Brompton National Heart Hospital. USA: Lately Fellow, University of California Medical Center, San Francisco.*

FITZHARRIS, Dr Penny F.

Especially pollen allergies.
PRIVATE: Refer to address and number below.
NHS: Consultant Physician, Allergy Clinic,
St Mary's Hospital, Praed Street, London W2 1NY.
Tel: 071 725 1082. Fax: 071 725 1121.

ACADEMIC: Senior Lecturer, St Mary's. MAJOR DEGREES: MD, FRCAP. First qualified in New Zealand in 1972. Specialist training at the Royal Brompton and National Heart Hospital.

GEDDES, Dr Duncan M.

Especially cystic fibrosis.
Private: 28 Weymouth Street, London W1N 3FA.
Tel: 071 487 5550.
NHS: Consultant Physician, Royal Brompton National Heart and Lung Hospital, Fulham Road, London SW3 6HP.
Tel: 071 352 8121. Fax: 071 351 8099.

MAJOR DEGREES: MD, FRCP. First qualified (with honours) in Cambridge in 1971.

GREEN, Dr Malcolm.

PRIVATE: Lister Hospital, Chelsea Bridge Road,
London SW1W 8RH. Tel: 071 376 4985. Fax: 071 351 8331.
NHS: Consultant Physician in Charge, Royal Brompton
National Heart and Lung Hospital, Fulham Road,
London SW3 6HP. Tel: 071 352 8121. Fax: 071 351 8473.

ACADEMIC: Lately Dean, Institute of Thoracic Medicine. President, Postgraduate Medical Federation. DISTINCTION: Founder, British Lung Foundation. MAJOR DEGREES: DM, FRCP. First qualified in Oxford in 1965. Specialist training at the Westminster, St Bartholomew's and the Royal Brompton and National Heart Hospitals. USA: Lately Radcliffe Fellow, Harvard Medical School.

MOORE-GILLAN, Dr John C.

Especially asthma, lung cancer.
PRIVATE: Refer to address and number below.
NHS: Consultant Physician, Department of Respiratory Medicine, St Bartholomew's Hospital, West Smithfield, London EC1A 7BE. Tel: 071 601 8441. Fax: 071 601 8444.

ACADEMIC: Senior Lecturer in Respiratory Medicine, St Bartholomew's. MAJOR DEGREES: FRCP, MD. First qualified in Cambridge in 1976. Specialist training in Cambridge and at St Thomas's Hospital.

SCADDING, Dr Glenys K.

Rhinitis.
PRIVATE: Refer to address and number below.
NHS: Consultant Rhinologist, Royal National Throat, Nose and Ear Hospital, Gray's Inn Road, London WC1X 8DA. Tel: 071 837 8855. Fax: 071 833 5518.

MAJOR DEGREES: MD, FRCP. First qualified in Cambridge in 1973. Specialist training at the Middlesex and the Royal Brompton and National Heart Hospitals.

SPIRO, Dr Stephen G.

Especially diagnosis and management of lung cancer.
PRIVATE: Refer to address and number below.
NHS: Consultant Physician, University College Hospital,
Gower Street, London WC1E 6AU. Tel: 071 387 9300.

ACADEMIC: Senior Lecturer, Institute of Thoracic Medicine.
DISTINCTION: Chairman of the Thoracic Oncology Division of
the Societies Europea Pneunologica. MAJOR DEGREES: MD,
FRCP. First qualified in Manchester in 1967. Specialist train-
ing at the Royal Free Hospital and the Royal Postgraduate
Medical School. USA: Lately Senior Research Fellow in
Respiratory Diseases, University of Washington, Seattle.

CHEST (THORACIC/LUNG) SURGEONS

DUSSEK, Mr Julian E.

PRIVATE: Emblem House, London Bridge Hospital,
27 Tooley Street, London SE1 2PR.
Tel: 071 403 4884. Fax: 071 407 3162.
NHS: Consultant Thoracic Surgeon, Guy's Hospital,
St Thomas' Street, London SE1 9RT. Tel: 071 955 5000.

MAJOR DEGREE: FRCS. *First qualified in London in 1967.*
Specialist training at the National Heart, Guy's and St
Thomas's Hospitals.

GOLDSTRAW, Mr Peter.

PRIVATE: Refer to address and number below.
NHS: Consultant Thoracic Surgeon, University College
Hospital, Gower Street, London WC1E 6AU.
Tel: 071 387 9300. Fax: 071 380 9977.

MAJOR DEGREE: FRCS. *First qualified in Birmingham in 1968.*
Specialist training at the Royal Infirmary, Edinburgh, and
Glasgow University Medical College.

KAPLAN, Mr David K.

PRIVATE: Refer to address and number below.
NHS: Consultant Thoracic Surgeon, Royal Brompton
National Heart and Lung Hospital, Fulham Road,
London SW3 6HP. Tel: 071 352 8121. Fax 071 351 8099.

ACADEMIC: *Senior Lecturer, National Heart and Lung*
Institute. MAJOR DEGREE: FRCS. *First qualified in London in*
1980. Specialist training at Northern General Infirmary,
Sheffield, and Liverpool Royal Infirmary.

PATTISON, Mr Charles W.

PRIVATE: Refer to address and number below.
NHS: Middlesex Hospital, Mortimer Street, London
W1N 8AA. Tel: 071 636 8333. Fax: 071 323 0397.

MAJOR DEGREE: *FRCS First qualified in Birmingham in 1980. Specialist training at Harefield, the Royal Brompton National Heart and Lung and St Thomas's Hospitals.*

SMITH, Mr Peter L. C.

PRIVATE: Refer to address and number below.
NHS: Consultant Surgeon, Cardiothoracic Unit,
Hammersmith Hospital, 150 Du Cane Road,
London W12 0HS. Tel: 081 740 3125. Fax: 081 740 3719.

DISTINCTION: *Lately Huntingdon Professor, Royal College of Surgeons.* MAJOR DEGREES: *FRCP, FRCS. First qualified in London in 1975. Specialist training at the Royal Postgraduate Medical School and Harefield Hospital.*

COLORECTAL SURGEONS

HAWLEY, Mr Peter.

PRIVATE: 149 Harley Street, London W1N 2DE.
Tel: 071 935 4444. Fax: 071 486 3782.
NHS: Consultant Surgeon, St Mark's Hospital, City Road,
London EC1V 2PS Tel: 071 253 1050. Fax: 071 601 7973.

*DISTINCTION: Consultant Colon and Rectal Surgeon to the
Army. MAJOR DEGREES: MS, FRCS. First qualified in London
in 1956. Specialist training at St Mark's. USA: Lately Research
Fellow in Surgery, University of California, San Francisco.*

LEWIS, Mr Anthony A.

Especially bowel surgery.
PRIVATE: 112 Harley Street, London W1N 1AF.
Tel: 071 935 1956.
NHS: Consultant Surgeon, Royal Free Hospital, Pond Street,
London NW3 2QG. Tel: 071 794 0500. Fax: 071 435 5342.

*MAJOR DEGREE: FRCS. First qualified in London in 1963.
Specialist training at the Royal Free Hospital. USA: Stanford
University Medical School, California.*

NICHOLLS, Mr R. John.

PRIVATE: 149 Harley Street, London W1N 2DE.
Tel: 071 935 4444. Fax: 071 486 3782.
NHS: Consultant Surgeon, St Thomas's Hospital,
Lambeth Palace Road, London SE1 7EH.
Tel: 071 928 9292. Fax: 071 922 8079.
and St Mark's Hospital, City Road, London EC1V 2PS.
Tel: 071 253 1050. Fax: 071 601 7973.

ACADEMIC: Lately Senior Lecturer, St Bartholomew's Hospital.

DISTINCTION: *Lately Hallet Prize, Royal College of Surgeons.* MAJOR DEGREE: *FRCS. First qualified in Cambridge in 1968. Specialist training at St Bartholomew's and the London Hospitals and in Heidelberg, Germany.*

NORTHOVER, Mr John M. A.

PRIVATE: Refer to address and number below.
NHS: Consultant Surgeon, St Mark's Hospital, City Road, London EC1V 2PS. Tel: 071 253 1050. Fax: 071 601 7973.

ACADEMIC: *Director, Imperial Cancer Research Fund Colorectal Research Unit.* MAJOR DEGREE: *FRCS. First qualified in London in 1970. Specialist training at St Mark's Hospital.*

SHAND, Mr William S.

PRIVATE: 149 Harley Street, London WIN 2DE.
NHS: Consultant Surgeon, St Bartholomew's Hospital, West Smithfield, London EC1A 7BE.
Tel: 071 601 8888. Fax: 071 601 7899.

DISTINCTIONS: *Honorary Consultant Surgeon, St Mark's Hospital; Court of Examiners, Royal College of Surgeons, England and Edinburgh.* MAJOR DEGREES: *MD, FRCS. First qualified in Cambridge in 1962. Specialist training at St Mark's and St Bartholomew's Hospitals.*

SPRINGALL, Mr Roger G.

PRIVATE: 149 Harley Street, London W1N 1HG.
Tel: 071 486 7927. Fax: 071 486 3782.
NHS: Consultant Surgeon, Charing Cross Hospital,
Fulham Palace Road, London W6 8RF.
Tel: 081 846 1234. Fax: 081 846 1111.

MAJOR DEGREES: *ChM, FRCS. First qualified in Liverpool 1973. Specialist training at St Bartholomew's and St Mark's Hospitals.*

THOMSON, Mr James P. S.

PRIVATE: 149 Harley Street. London W1N 1HG
Tel: 071 935 4444. Fax: 071 486 3782.
NHS: Clinical Director and Consultant Surgeon,
St Mark's Hospital, City Road, London EC1V 2PS.
Tel: 071 253 1050. Fax: 071 601 7973.

DISTINCTIONS: *Consultant Surgeon to the Royal Navy and the Royal Air Force; Examiner, Universities of Cambridge and London and the Royal College of Surgeons.* MAJOR DEGREES: *FRCS, MS. First qualified in London in 1962. Specialist training at the Middlesex and St Mark's Hospitals.*

DERMATOLOGISTS

ATHERTON, Dr David.

Children.
Private: Refer to address and number below.
NHS: Consultant Dermatologist, Hospital for Sick Children,
34 Great Ormond Street, London WC1N 3JH.
Tel: 071 405 9200. Fax: 071 829 8634.

ACADEMIC: *Senior Lecturer, Institute of Child Health.* MAJOR
DEGREE: *FRCP. First qualified in Cambridge in 1974.*
Specialist training at Guy's Hospital.

BLACK, Dr Martin M.

PRIVATE: York House, 199 Westminster Bridge Road,
London SE1 7UT. Tel: 071 928 5485. Fax: 071 928 3748.
NHS: Consultant, St John's Dermatology Centre,
St Thomas's Hospital, Lambeth Palace Road,
London SE1 7EH. Tel: 071 928 9292. Fax 071 922 8079.

ACADEMIC: *Senior Lecturer, Histopath Institute of Dermatology,*
London. DISTINCTIONS: *Consultant Dermatologist to the Army;*
President, Institute of Dermatological Pathology. MAJOR
DEGREES: *MD, FRCP. First qualified in Durham in 1963.*
Specialist training at the Institute of Dermatology, London, and
the Royal Victoria Infirmary, Newcastle. USA: Gold Award,
American Academy of Dermatology.

BUNKER, Dr Christopher B.

PRIVATE: Refer to address and number below.
NHS: Consultant Dermatologist, Chelsea and Westminster
Hospital, 369 Fulham Road, London, SW10 9NH.
Tel: 081 746 8000. Fax: 081 746 8111.

MAJOR DEGREE: *FRCP. First qualified in London in 1981.*

du VIVIER, Dr Anthony W.

Especially pigmented moles.
PRIVATE: 115a Harley Street, London W1N 1DG.
Tel: 071 935 6465.
NHS: Consultant Dermatologist, King's College Hospital,
Denmark Hill, London SE5 9RS. Tel: 071 274 6222.

*MAJOR DEGREES: MD, FRCP. First qualified in 1968. Specialist
training at St Mary's and St Bartholomew's Hospitals.
USA: Research Fellow, Scripps Clinic, La Jolla, California.*

GILKES, Dr Jeremy J. H.

Especially skin diseases of the mouth.
PRIVATE: 115a Harley Street, London W1N 1DG.
Tel: 071 935 6465.
NHS: Consultant Dermatologist, Middlesex Hospital,
Mortimer Street, London W1N 8AA.
Tel: 071 636 8333. Fax: 071 323 0397
and Eastman Dental Hospital, Gray's Inn Road,
London WC1X 8LD. Tel: 071 837 3646.

*ACADEMIC: Senior Lecturer in Dermatology, University
College. MAJOR DEGREES: MD, FRCP. First qualified in
London in 1964. Specialist training at Guy's and
St Bartholomew's Hospitals.*

GRIFFITHS, Dr William A. D.

Especially industrial skin diseases.
PRIVATE: 6 Harley Street, London W1N 1AA.
Tel: 071 631 3459.
NHS: Consultant Dermatologist, St John's Dermatology
Centre, St Thomas's Hospital, Lambeth Palace Road,
London SE1 7EH. Tel: 071 928 9292. Fax: 071 922 8079.

MAJOR DEGREES: MD, FRCP. First qualified in Liverpool in 1965. Specialist training in Cambridge and Liverpool.

HARPER, Dr John I.

Children.
PRIVATE: Refer to address and number below.
NHS: Consultant Paediatric Dermatologist, Hospital for Sick Children, 34 Great Ormond Street, London WC1N 3JH.
Tel: 071 405 9200. Fax: 071 829 8643.

DISTINCTION: Author, standard work on paediatric dermatology. MAJOR DEGREES: MD, FRCP. First qualified in 1973.

LEONARD, Dr Jonathan.

Especially blistering.
PRIVATE: 152 Harley Street, London W1N 1HH.
Tel: 071 935 2477.
NHS: Consultant Dermatologist, St Mary's Hospital, Praed Street, London W2 1NY.
Tel: 071 262 1280 or 725 6666. Fax: 071 725 6200.

MAJOR DEGREES: MD, FRCP. First qualified in London in 1975. Specialist training in Oxford, and at St Mary's Hospital.

LEIGH, Professor Irene M.

Laboratory cultivation of patient's own skin for grafting.
PRIVATE: Refer to address and number below.
NHS AND ACADEMIC: Professor of Dermatology, Department of Experimental Dermatology, Royal London Hospital, Whitechapel, London E1 1BB.
Tel: 071 377 7749. Fax: 071 377 6509.

MAJOR DEGREE: MD, FRCP. First qualified in London in 1971. Specialist training at St John's and the Middlesex Hospitals.

LEVENE, Dr Gerald M.

Especially blistering.
PRIVATE: 152 Harley Street, London W1N 1HH.
Tel: 071 935 1858.
NHS: Consultant Dermatologist, Middlesex Hospital, Mortimer Street, London W1N 8AA.
Tel: 071 636 8333. Fax: 071 323 0397.

ACADEMIC: Lately Senior Lecturer, Royal Postgraduate Medical School and the Institute of Dermatology. DISTINCTIONS: Civil Consultant in Dermatology to the Royal Air Force; lately President, St John's Hospital Dermatological Society and British Association of Dermatologists. MAJOR DEGREE: FRCP. First qualified (with honours) in 1959. Specialist training at St John's and the Institute of Dermatology.

MAYOU, Dr Susan C.

Children's skin problems.
PRIVATE: Refer to address and number below.
NHS: Consultant Dermatologist, Chelsea and Westminster Hospital, 369 Fulham Road, London SW10 9NH.
Tel: 081 746 8000. Fax: 081 746 8111.

MAJOR DEGREE: MRCP. First qualified in London in 1977. Specialist training at St Thomas's and St Bartholemew's Hospitals.

PEMBROKE, Dr Andrew C.

Private: 152 Harley Street, London W1N 1HH.
Tel: 071 935 2477.
NHS: Consultant Dermatologist, King's College Hospital,
Denmark Hill, London SE5 9RS. Tel: 071 274 6222.

MAJOR DEGREE: FRCP. First qualified in 1971. Specialist training at King's College and the Royal London Hospitals.

ROBINSON, Dr Trevor W.

PRIVATE: 18 Wimpole Street, London W1M 7TB.
Tel: 071 387 2160.
NHS: Consultant, University College Hospital, Gower Street,
London WC1E 6AU. Tel: 071 387 9300. Fax: 071 380 9977.

MAJOR DEGREES: MD, FRCP. First qualified in 1959. Specialist training at St Bartholomew's and St John's Hospitals.

RUSTIN, Dr Malcolm H. A.

Especially sclerosis.
PRIVATE. Refer to address and number below.
NHS: Royal Free Hospital, Pond Street, London NW3 2QG.
Tel: 071 794 0500. Fax: 071 435 5342.

MAJOR DEGREES: MD, FRCP. First qualified in 1976.

STAUGHTON, Dr Richard C.

Including dermatological aspects of AIDS.
PRIVATE: Lister Hospital, Chelsea Bridge Road, SW1W 8RH.
Tel: 071 730 3417. Fax: 071 824 8867.
NHS: Consultant, Chelsea and Westminster Hospital,
369 Fulham Road, London, SW10 9NH.
Tel: 081 746 8000. Fax: 081 746 8111.

DISTINCTION: *Consultant Dermatologist to the Royal Navy.*
MAJOR DEGREE: *FRCP. First qualified in 1970. Specialist training at Cambridge and St Thomas's Hospital.*

DIABETOLOGISTS

BARNES, Dr Adrian J.

Especially glandular aspects.
PRIVATE: Refer to address and number below.
NHS: Consultant Physician, Barnet General Hospital,
Wellhouse Lane, Barnet, Herts EN5 3DJ. Tel: 071 440 5111.

MAJOR DEGREES: *MD, FRCP. First qualified in London in
1971. Specialist training at the Royal Postgraduate Medical
School.*

ELKELES, Dr Robert S.

PRIVATE: Consulting Rooms, Humana Hospital Wellington,
Wellington Place, London NW8 9LE.
Tel: 071 586 3213 Fax: 071 483 0297.
NHS: Consultant Physician, St Mary's Hospital, Praed Street,
London W2 1NY. Tel: 071 262 1280. Fax: 071 725 6200.

MAJOR DEGREES: *MD, FRCP. First qualified in Cardiff in
1965. Specialist training at University Hospital, Cardiff, the
Medical Research Council, and the Royal Postgraduate
Medical School.*

GALE, Professor Edwin

PRIVATE: Refer to address and number below.
NHS: Consultant Physician, St Bartholomew's Hospital,
West Smithfield, London, EC1A 7BE.
Tel: 071 601 8888. Fax: 071 601 7899.

ACADEMIC: *Professor of Diabetes and Immunogenetics,
Medical College of St Bartholomew's.* MAJOR DEGREE: *FRCP.
First qualified in Cambridge in 1973. Specialist training at
Oxford Diabetes Unit and St Bartholomew's Hospital.*

KURTZ, Dr Anthony B.

PRIVATE: Refer to address and number below.
NHS: Consultant Physician, Middlesex Hospital,
Mortimer Street, London W1N 8AA.
Tel: 071 380 9109. Fax: 071 436 1536.

ACADEMIC: *Reader in Diabetic Medicine, Middlesex and
University College Medical Schools. First qualified in
Cambridge in 1965. Specialist training at the Middlesex.*

McHARDY-YOUNG, Dr Stuart.

PRIVATE: 106 Harley Street, London W1N 1AF.
Tel: 071 935 2797.
NHS: Consultant Physician, Central Middlesex Hospital,
Acton Lane, Park Royal, London NW1O 7NS.
Tel: 081 965 5733.

DISTINCTION: *Consultant, Royal Postgraduate Medical School.*
MAJOR DEGREES: *MD, FRCP. First qualified in London in
1960. Specialist training at Guy's. USA: Lately Fellow,
Stanford University School of Medicine, California.*

SONKSEN, Professor Peter S.

Pituitary disorders.
PRIVATE: Refer to address and number below.
NHS: Consultant Physician, St Thomas's Hospital,
Lambeth Palace Road, London SE1 7EH.
Tel: 071 928 9292. Fax: 071 922 8079.

ACADEMIC: *Professor of Endocrinology, Guy's and
St Thomas's United Medical Schools.* MAJOR DEGREES: *MD,
FRCP. First qualified in London in 1960. Specialist training at
the Middlesex Hospital. USA: Lately Harkness Fellow,
Harvard University.*

YUDKIN, Professor John S.

Takes no new cases. Respected second opinion.
NHS AND ACADEMIC: Professor of Medicine, Whittington
Hospital, Highgate Hill, London N19 5NF.
Tel: 071 288 5301. Fax: 071 288 5302.

*MAJOR DEGREES: MD, FRCP. First qualified in Cambridge in
1967. Specialist training at the Royal London Hospital.*

WATKINS, Dr Peter J.

PRIVATE: Refer to address and number below.
NHS: Consultant Diabetologist, King's College Hospital,
Denmark Hill, London SE59RS.
Tel: 071 274 6222. Fax: 071 326 3589.

*MAJOR DEGREES: MD, FRCP. First qualified in 1961. Specialist
training in Birmingham and at St Bartholomew's Hospital.*

DIAGNOSTIC RADIOLOGISTS

BARTRAM, Dr Clive I.

Especially gastrointestinal barium investigation.
PRIVATE: Refer to address and number below.
NHS: Consultant Radiologist, St Bartholomew's Hospital,
West Smithfield, London EC1A 7BE
Tel: 071 601 8888. Fax: 071 601 7899.

*MAJOR DEGREES: FRCP, FRCR. First qualified in London in
1966. Specialist training at St Mark's and St Bartholomew's
Hospitals.*

GISHEN, Dr Philip.

Especially keyhole radiology, including of lungs.
PRIVATE: X-Ray Department, Devonshire Hospital,
29 Devonshire Street, London W1N 1RF.
Tel: 071 486 2524. Fax: 071 486 0090.
NHS: Consultant Radiologist, King's College Hospital,
Denmark Hill, London SE5 9RS.
Tel: 071 274 6222. Fax: 071 326 3589.

*MAJOR DEGREE: FRCR. First qualified in Witwatersrand,
South Africa in 1968. Specialist training at Johannesburg
General and King's College Hospitals.*

LEES, Dr William R.

Gastrointestinal ultrasound.
PRIVATE: Refer to address and number below.
NHS: Consultant Radiologist, Middlesex Hospital,
Mortimer Street, London W1N 8AA.
Tel: 071 636 8333. Fax: 071 323 0397.

*MAJOR DEGREE: FRCR. First qualified in London in 1972.
Specialist training at the Middlesex Hospital.*

LONGMORE, Professor Donald.

Especially non-intrusive investigations of the heart.
NHS AND ACADEMIC: Director, Magnetic Resonance Unit,
Royal Brompton National Heart and Lung Hospital,
Fulham Road, London SW3 6UP
Tel: 071 352 8121. Fax: 071 351 8099.

MAJOR DEGREE: FRCS. First qualified in London in 1953.

McLEAN, Dr Alison M.

Gastrointestinal barium, ultrasound and CT scanning.
PRIVATE: Refer to address and number below.
NHS: Consultant Radiologist, St Bartholomew's Hospital,
West Smithfield, London EC1A 7BE
Tel: 071 601 8888. Fax: 071 601 7899.

*MAJOR DEGREES: FRCP, FRCR. First qualified in Cambridge
in 1975. Specialist training at St Bartholomew's. USA: Clinical
Fellow, New England Hospital, Boston, Massachusetts.*

MAISEY, Professor Michael

Especially investigations of the thyroid and other glands.
PRIVATE: Refer to address and number below.
NHS AND ACADEMIC: Professor of Radiology, Guy's Hospital,
St Thomas Sreet, London SE1 9RT. Tel: 071 955 5000.

*DISTINCTION: Consultant to the Army. Major degrees: MD,
FRCP, FRCR. First qualified in London in 1964. Specialist
training at Guy's. USA: Lately Research Fellow in Nuclear
Medicine, Johns Hopkins, Baltimore, Maryland.*

RICKARDS, Dr David.

Ultrasound and CT scans of male genital and urinary organs.
PRIVATE: 64 Harley Street, London W1N 1AE.
Tel: 071 637 8207. Fax: 071 436 7059.
NHS: Consultant Radiologist, Middlesex Hospital,
Mortimer Street, London W1N 8AA.
Tel: 071 636 8333. Fax: 071 323 0397.

ACADEMIC: *Senior Lecturer, Institute of Urology.* MAJOR
DEGREES: *FRCR, FFR. First qualified in South Africa in 1972.*
Specialist training at Manchester University and the
Middlesex.

WESTABY, Dr David.

Endoscopic investigation.
PRIVATE: The Cromwell Hospital, Cromwell Road, London
SW5 0TU.
Tel: 071 370 4233 Fax: 071 370 4063.
NHS: Consultant Physician, The Liver Unit,
King's College Hospital, Denmark Hill, London SE5 9RS.
Tel: 071 274 6222. Fax: 071 326 3589.

MAJOR DEGREE: *FRCP. First qualified in Cambridge in 1976.*
Specialist training at King's College Hospital.

EAR, NOSE AND THROAT SPECIALISTS

BAILEY, Mr C. Martin.

Paediatric surgeon.
PRIVATE: 56 Harley Street, London W1N 1DD.
Tel: 071 580 2426.
NHS: Consultant ENT Surgeon, Hospital for Sick Children,
34 Great Ormond Street, London WCIN 3JH.
Tel: 071 405 9200 Fax: 071 829 8643

ACADEMIC: *Senior Lecturer, Institute of Child Health and
Institute of Laryngology and Otology. MAJOR DEGREE: FRCS.
First qualified in London in 1973. Specialist training at the
Sussex Throat and Ear Hospital and the Royal National
Throat, Nose and Ear Hospital.*

BELLMAN, Dr Susan C.

Paediatric audiological physician.
PRIVATE: Refer to address and number below.
NHS: Hospital for Sick Children, 34 Great Ormond Street,
London WC1N 3JH.
Tel: 071 405 9200. Fax: 071 829 8643.

MAJOR DEGREE: *FRCS. First qualified in Cambridge in 1972.
Specialist training at the Royal National Throat, Nose and Ear
Hospital.*

BOOTH, Mr John B.

The voice.
PRIVATE: 18 Upper Wimpole Street, London W1M 7TB.
Tel: 071 935 1304 Fax: 071 224 1969.
NHS: Consultant ENT Surgeon, Royal London Hospital,
Whitechapel, London E1 1BB.
Tel: 071 377 7000. Fax: 071 377 7396 or 7122.

ACADEMIC: *Lecturer, Institute of Laryngology and Otology.*

DISTINCTIONS: Civilian Consultant to the Royal Air Force; Laryngologist to the Royal Opera House and the Royal College of Music. MAJOR DEGREE: FRCS. First qualified in London in 1963. Specialist training at the Royal Free and Royal National Throat, Nose and Ear Hospitals.

BULL, Mr Tony R.

Rhinoplasty.
PRIVATE: 107 Harley Street, London W1N 1DG.
Tel: 071 935 3171.
NHS: Consultant ENT Surgeon, Charing Cross Hospital, Fulham Palace Road, London W6 8RF.
Tel: 081 846 1234. Fax: 081 846 1111.

DISTINCTION: Lately Yearsley Lecturer, Royal Society of Medicine. MAJOR DEGREE: FRCS. First qualified in London in 1958. Specialist training at the London Hospital and the Royal National Throat, Nose and Ear Hospital.
USA: Lately Senior Fellow in Otology, Memphis Foundation.

CHEESMAN, Mr Anthony D.

Head and neck.
PRIVATE: 128 Harley Street, London WIN 1AH.
Tel: 071 370 2835.
NHS: Consultant Otolaryngolist, Charing Cross Hospital, Fulham Palace Road, London W6 8RF.
Tel: 081 846 1234. Fax: 081 846 1111.

MAJOR DEGREE: FRCS. First qualified in London in 1965. Specialist training at the Royal National Throat, Nose and Ear Hospital.

CROFT, Mr Charles B.

Sleep apnoea, snoring, head and neck surgery.
PRIVATE: 144 Harley Street, London W1N 1DD.
Tel: 071 580 2426
NHS: Consultant ENT Surgeon, Royal National Throat, Nose
and Ear Hospital, Gray's Inn Road, London WC1X 8DA.
Tel: 071 837 8855. Fax: 071 833 5518.

*DISTINCTIONS: Civil Consultant to the Royal Air Force;
Examiner, Royal College of Surgeons, Edinburgh. MAJOR
DEGREE: FRCS. First qualified (with honours) in Leeds in
1965. Specialist training at Leeds General Infirmary.
USA: Lately Associate Professor, Albert Einstein Medical
School, New York.*

DOUEK, Mr Ellis E.

Nose, sense of smell.
PRIVATE: 97 Harley Street, London W1N 1DF.
Tel: 071 935 7828.
NHS: Consultant Otologist, Guy's Hospital,
London SE1 9RT. Tel: 071 407 7600.

*MAJOR DEGREE: FRCS. First qualified in London in 1958.
Specialist training at University College Hospital.*

FRASER, Mr James G. F.

Profound hearing loss.
PRIVATE: 16 Upper Wimpole Street, London W1N 7TB.
Tel: 071 935 7435.
NHS: Consultant ENT Surgeon, University College Hospital,
Gower Street, London WC1E 6AU.
Tel: 071 387 9300. Fax: 071 380 9977.

MAJOR DEGREE: FRCS. First qualified in Oxford in 1961.

GARFIELD DAVIES, Mr David.

Vocal cords.
PRIVATE: 149 Harley Street, London W1N 1HG.
Tel: 071 935 4444.
NHS: Director, Voice Clinic, Ferens Institute of
Otolaryngology, Middlesex Hospital, Mortimer Street,
London W1N 8AA. Tel: 071 380 9362. Fax: 071 436 0184.

MAJOR DEGREE: FRCS. First qualified in London in 1959.
Specialist training at the Royal National Throat, Nose and Ear
Hospital. USA: Lately Fellow in Otology at Massachusetts Eye
and Ear Hospital, Boston.

HAZELL, Mr Jonathan W. P.

Tinnitus.
PRIVATE: 32 Devonshire Place, London W1N 1PE.
Tel: 071 935 0328.
NHS: Consultant in Neuro-Otology, University College
Hospital, Gower Street, London WC1E 6AU.
Tel: 071 387 9300. Fax: 071 380 9977.

DISTINCTION: Consultant in Neuro-Otology, Royal National
Institute for the Deaf. MAJOR DEGREE: FRCS. First qualified in
Cambridge in 1966. Specialist training at the Royal National
Throat, Nose and Ear Hospital.

KEENE, Mr Malcolm Howard.

Head and neck surgery.
PRIVATE: 48 Wimpole Street, London W1M 7DG.
Tel: 071 486 0697.
NHS: Consultant ENT Surgeon, St Bartholomew's Hospital,
West Smithfield, London EC1A 7BE.
Tel: 071 601 8888. Fax: 071 601 7899.

MAJOR DEGREE: FRCS. First qualified in London in 1970.

Specialist training at the Middlesex and Royal Throat, Nose and Ear Hospitals, London and the University of Toronto, Canada.

LAVELLE, Mr Richard J.

Surgery of the larynx.
PRIVATE: 86 Harley Street, London W1N 1AE.
Tel: 071 580 3625.
NHS: Consultant ENT Surgeon, St Bartholomew's Hospital, West Smithfield, London EC1A 7BE.
Tel: 071 601 8888. Fax: 071 601 7899.

MAJOR DEGREE: FRCS. First qualified in London in 1962. Specialist training at the Royal National Throat, Nose and Ear and Royal Marsden Hospitals.

LUDMAN, Mr Harold.

Otology and neuro-otology.
PRIVATE: 149 Harley Street, London W1N 2DE.
Tel: 071 935 4444. Fax: 071 486 3782.
NHS: Consultant Surgeon, King's College Hospital, Denmark Hill, London SE5 9RS.
Tel: 071 274 6222. Fax: 071 326 3438.

DISTINCTION: Lately President, Otolaryngology Section, Royal Society of Medicine. MAJOR DEGREE: FRCS. First qualified (with first-class honours in natural science) in Cambridge in 1957. Specialist training at King's College Hospital.

LUND, Miss Valerie J.

Sinusitis.
PRIVATE: Refer to address and number below.
NHS AND ACADEMIC: Senior Lecturer, Professorial Unit,
Royal National Throat, Nose and Ear Hospital,
Gray's Inn Road, London WC1X 8DA.
Tel: 071 837 8855. Fax: 071 833 5518.

MAJOR DEGREES: MS, FRCS. First qualified in London in 1971.
Specialist training at the Royal National Throat, Nose and Ear
Hospital.

LUXON, Dr Linda.

Neuro-otological physician.
PRIVATE: 47 Weymouth Street, London W1N 3LD.
Tel: 071 486 5787.
NHS: Consultant Physician, National Hospital,
Queen Square, London WC1N 3BJ.
Tel: 071 837 3611. Fax: 071 829 8720.

MAJOR DEGREE: FRCP. First qualified in London in 1972.
Specialist training at the National Hospital.

MACKAY, Mr Ian S.

Rhinoplasty.
PRIVATE: 55 Harley Street, London W1N 1ED.
Tel: 071 580 5070
NHS: Consultant ENT Surgeon, Chelsea and Westminster
Hospital, 369 Fulham Road, London SW10 9NH.
Tel: 081 746 8000. Fax: 081 746 8111.

ACADEMIC: Senior Lecturer, Royal National Throat, Nose and
Ear Hospital. MAJOR DEGREE: FRCS. First qualified in London
in 1968. Specialist training at the Royal National Throat,
Nose and Ear Hospital.

SHAH, Mr Navnit.

Deafness, glue ear, middle-ear surgery.
PRIVATE: 80 Harley Street, London W1N 1AE.
Tel: 071 580 3664.
NHS: Consultant Surgeon, Royal National Throat, Nose and
Ear Hospital, Gray's Inn Road, London WC1X 8DA.
Tel: 071 837 8855. Fax: 071 833 5518.

ACADEMIC: *Lately Vice-Dean, Institute of Laryngology and
Otology.* DISTINCTIONS: *President, ENT Section, Royal Society
of Medicine; Honorary Professor, Portman Foundation,
Bordeaux, France.* MAJOR DEGREE: *FRCS. First qualified in
Bombay, India in 1958. Specialist training at the Royal
National Throat, Nose and Ear Hospital.*

WALSH-WARING, Mr Gerald F.

Head and neck surgery.
PRIVATE: 2 Upper Wimpole Street, London W1M 7TD.
Tel: 071 935 6172.
NHS: Consultant in Charge, Head and Neck Oncology,
St Mary's and Hammersmith hospitals, St Mary's Hospital,
Praed Street, London W2 1NY.
Tel: 071 262 1280 or 725 6666. Fax: 071 725 6200.

MAJOR DEGREE: *FRCS. First qualified in London in 1958.
Specialist training at St Mary's and the Royal Marsden Hospitals.*

WRIGHT, Professor Anthony.

Vertigo, dizziness, loss of sense of balance.
PRIVATE: Refer to address and number below.
NHS AND ACADEMIC: Director, Institute of Laryngology and
Otology, Royal National Throat, Nose and Ear Hospital,
Gray's Inn Road, London WC1X 8DA.
Tel: 071 837 8855. Fax: 071 833 5518.

Major degree: FRCS. First qualified in Oxford in 1974.

ENDOCRINOLOGISTS

BESSER, Professor Michael G.

Pituitary and thyroid disorders, impotence, hirsutism.
PRIVATE: Refer to address and number below.
NHS: Consultant Physician, St Bartholomew's Hospital,
West Smithfield, London EC1A 7BE.
Tel (direct): 071 601 8344. Fax (direct): 071 601 8505.

ACADEMIC: *Professor of Medicine, Medical College of
St Bartholomew's.* DISTINCTIONS: *Consultant Endocrinologist
to the Royal Navy; Honorary Member, American Association
of Physicians; President, Endocrine Section, Royal Society of
Medicine; Censor, Royal College of Physicians; Honorary
Doctor of University of Turin, Italy.* MAJOR DEGREES: *DSc,
MD, FRCP. First qualified (with distinctions in medicine and
surgery) in London in 1960. Specialist training at the Royal
Brompton and National Heart Hospitals, the Royal
Postgraduate Medical School and St Bartholomew's Hospital.*

BLOOM, Professor Stephen R.

Gastrointestinal hormones.
PRIVATE: Refer to address and number below.
NHS: Consultant, Hammersmith Hospital,
150 Du Cane Road, London W12 0HS.
Tel: 071 743 2030. Fax: 081 740 3169.

ACADEMIC: *Professor of Endocrinology, Royal Postgraduate
Medical School.* MAJOR DEGREES: *DSc, MD, FRCP. First qual-
ified in Cambridge in 1967. Specialist training at the
Middlesex Hospital.*

BROOK, Professor Charles G. D.

Children's growth and development.
PRIVATE: Refer to address and number below.
NHS: Consultant Paediatrician, Middlesex Hospital,
Mortimer Street, London W1N 8AA.
Tel: 071 636 8333 Fax: 071 323 0397.

ACADEMIC: *Professor of Paediatric Endocrinology, Middlesex Hospital Medical School. MAJOR DEGREES: MD, FRCP. First qualified in Cambridge in 1964. Specialist training at the Middlesex Hospital.*

FRANKS, Professor Stephen.

Hormonal aspects of gynaecology and fertility.
PRIVATE: Refer to address and number below.
NHS: Consultant Physician, St Mary's Hospital,
Praed Street, London W2 1NY.
Tel: 071 262 1280 or 725 6666. Fax: 071 725 6200.

ACADEMIC: *Professor of Reproductive Endocrinology, St Mary's Medical School. MAJOR DEGREES: MD, FRCP. First qualified in Birmingham in 1970. Specialist training at Queen Elizabeth Hospital, Birmingham, McGill University, Canada, and the Middlesex Hospital.*

GROSSMAN, Dr Ashley B.

Pituitary and thyroid disorders, impotence, hirsutism.
PRIVATE: Refer to address and number below.
NHS: Consultant Physician, St Bartholomew's Hospital,
West Smithfield, London EC1A 7BE.
Tel: 071 601 8343. Fax: 071 601 8505.

ACADEMIC: *Senior Lecturer, Medical College of St Bartholomew's. MAJOR DEGREES: MD, FRCP. First*

WATERSTONE'S
BOOKSELLERS

99/101 Old Brompton Road London SW7 3LE Telephone 071-581 8522

from Mrs E. K. Sanderson.

With Compliments

qualified (with honours) in London, in 1975. Specialist training at St Thomas's and the National Hospitals.

JACOBS, Professor Howard S.

Hormonal aspects of gynaecology and fertility.
PRIVATE: Refer to address and number below.
NHS: Consultant, Middlesex Hospital,
Mortimer Street, London W1N 8AA.
Tel: 071 636 8333. Fax: 071 323 0397.

ACADEMIC: *Professor of Reproductive Endocrinology, Middlesex Hospital Medical School. MAJOR DEGREES: MD, FRCP. First qualified in Cambridge in 1963. Specialist training at the Middlesex Hospital. USA: Lately Assistant Professor, University of California Medical School, Los Angeles.*

LATELYS, Professor John A. H.

Pituitary and thyroid disorders, impotence, hirsutism.
PRIVATE: Refer to address and number below.
NHS: Consultant Physician, St Bartholomew's Hospital,
West Smithfield, London EC1A 7BE.
Tel: 071 601 8346. Fax: 071 601 7024.

ACADEMIC: *Professor of Clinical Endocrinology, Medical College of St Bartholomew's. MAJOR DEGREES: MD, FRCP. First qualified in London in 1971. Specialist training at Guy's, King's College and St Bartholomew's Hospitals.*

SAVAGE, Dr Martin.

Children's growth and development.
PRIVATE: Refer to address and number below.

NHS: Consultant Paediatric Endocrinologist,
St Bartholomew's Hospital, West Smithfield,
London EC1A 7BE. Tel: 071 601 8888. Fax: 071 601 7899.

MAJOR DEGREES: MD, FRCP. First qualified in Cambridge in 1968. Specialist training at the Hospital for Sick Children, and Hospital St Vincent de Paul, Paris.

SONKSEN, Professor Peter S.

Pituitary disorders.
PRIVATE: Refer to address and number below.
NHS: Consultant Physician, St Thomas's Hospital,
Lambeth Palace Road, London SE1 7EH.
Tel: 071 928 9292. Fax: 071 922 8079.

ACADEMIC: Professor of Endocrinology, Guy's and St Thomas's United Medical Schools. MAJOR DEGREES: MD, FRCP. First qualified in London in 1960. Specialist training at the Middlesex Hospital. USA: Lately Harkness Fellow, Harvard University.

WASS, Professor John A. H.

Pituitary and thyroid disorders, impotence, hirsutism.
NHS AND ACADEMIC: Professor of Clinical Endocrinology,
St Bartholomew's Hospital, West Smithfield,
London EC1A 7BE. Tel: 071 601 8346. Fax: 071 601 7024.

MAJOR DEGREES: MD, FRCP First qualified in London in 1971. Specialist training at St Bartholomew's Hospital.

ENDOCRINE SURGEONS

BEAUGIE, Mr John M.

Especially thyroids.
PRIVATE: Consulting Rooms, Humana Hospital Wellington,
London NW8 9LE.Tel: 071 586 5959. Fax: 071 586 1960.
NHS: Consultant Surgeon, North Middlesex Hospital,
Sterling Way, Edmonton, London N18 1QX.
Tel: 081 807 3071.

*DISTINCTION: Lately Arris and Gayle Lecturer, Royal College
of Surgeons. MAJOR DEGREES: FRCS, MS. First qualified in
London in 1963. Specialist training at the Royal London
Hospital.*

LYNN, Mr John.

Glands.
PRIVATE: Refer to address and number below.
NHS: Consultant Oncological Surgeon, Royal Postgraduate
Medical School. Hammersmith Hospital, 150 Du Cane Road,
London W12 0HS. Tel: 081 743 2030. Fax: 081 740 3169.

*ACADEMIC: Senior Lecturer, Royal Postgraduate Medical
School. MAJOR DEGREE: FRCS. Specialist training at the Royal
Postgraduate Medical School.*

MAYNARD, Mr John D.

Especially salivary glands.
PRIVATE: 97 Harley Street, London W1N 1DF.
NHS: Consultant Surgeon, Guy's Hospital, St Thomas Street,
London SE1 9RT. Tel: 071 955 5000.

*DISTINCTIONS: Lately Hunterian Professor, Royal College of
Surgeons. Chairman, Salivary Gland Tumour Panel. MAJOR*

DEGREES: FRCS, MS. First qualified in London in 1954.
Specialist training at the Royal London and Guy's Hospitals.

ROSSWICK, Mr Robert P.

Thyroids.
PRIVATE: 79 Harley Street, London W1N 1DE.
Tel: 071 935 3046.
NHS: Consultant Surgeon, St George's Hospital,
Blackshaw Road, London SW17 0QT. Tel: 081 672 1255.

ACADEMIC: Senior Lecturer, St George's Hospital. MAJOR
DEGREES: MS, FRCS. First qualified in London in 1955.
Specialist training at St George's Hospital. USA: Lately Fellow
in Surgery, Presbyterian St Luke's Hospital, Chicago. Master
of Surgery, University of Illinois.

SHAHEEN, Mr Omar H.

Thyroids.
PRIVATE: Emblem House, London Bridge Hospital,
27 Tooley Street, London SE1 2PR.
Tel: 071 403 4884. Fax: 071 407 3162.
NHS: Consultant ENT Surgeon, Head and Neck Oncology
Clinic, and Thyroid Cancer Clinic Guy's Hospital,
St Thomas Street, London SE1 9RT. Tel: 071 955 5000.

MAJOR DEGREES: MS, FRCS. First qualified in London in
1954. Specialist training at Guy's and the Royal National
Throat, Nose and Ear Hospitals. USA: Lately Assistant
Professor, University Hospital, Iowa.

WILLIAMSON, Professor Robin C. N.

PRIVATE: Refer to address and number below.
NHS: Director of Surgery, Royal Postgraduate Medical
School, Hammersmith Hospital, Du Cane Road,
London W12 0NN. Tel: 081 740 3210 Fax: 081 740 3179.

DISTINCTION: *Lately Fulbright Hayes Scholar, Hunterian
Professor and Examiner, Royal College of Surgeons;
Moynihan Fellow, Association of Surgeons; Secretary,* British
Journal of Surgery. MAJOR DEGREES: *MD, FRCS. First
qualified in Cambridge in 1964. USA: Lately Clinical Research
Fellow, Harvard.*

ENDOSCOPISTS

FAIRCLOUGH, Dr Peter D.

PRIVATE: Endoscopy Unit, London Clinic,
20 Devonshire Place, London W1N 2DH.
Tel: 071 935 4444. Fax: 071 486 3782.
NHS: Consultant Physician, Department of Gastroenterology,
St Bartholomew's Hospital, London EC1A 7BE .
Tel: 071 601 8508. Fax: 071 601 8510.

*ACADEMIC: Senior Lecturer, St Bartholomew's Medical
College. DISTINCTION: Lately Wellcome Senior Clinical
Research Fellow. MAJOR DEGREES: MD, FRCP. First qualified
in London in 1979. Specialist training at St Mark's and
St Bartholomew's Hospitals.*

HATFIELD, Dr Adrian R. W.

ERCP and non-surgical treatments of the liver and pancreas.
PRIVATE: 149 Harley Street, London W1N 1HG.
Tel: 071 935 4444. Fax: 071 486 3782.
NHS: Consultant Gastroenterologist, Middlesex Hospital,
Mortimer Street, London W1N 8AA.
Tel: 071 636 8333. Fax: 071 323 0397.

*MAJOR DEGREES: MD, FRCP. First qualified in London in
1969. Specialist training at the Middlesex and Royal London
Hospitals.*

WILLIAMS, Dr Christopher.

Especially colonoscopies, including children.
PRIVATE: London Clinic, 20 Devonshire Place, London
W1N 2DH. Tel: 071 935 4444. Fax: 071 486 3782.
NHS: Consultant Physician, Endoscopy Unit,

St Mark's Hospital, City Road, London EC1V 2PS.
Tel: 071 601 7919. Fax: 071 601 7973.
and the Hospital for Sick Children, 34 Great Ormond Street,
London WC1N 3JH.
Tel: 071 405 9200. Fax: 071 829 8643.

*MAJOR DEGREE: FRCP. First qualified in Oxford in 1964.
Specialist training at St Mark's and St Bartholomew's
Hospitals.*

GASTROENTEROLOGISTS

BOWN, Professor Stephen G.

Laser treatment of gastroenterological disorders.
PRIVATE: Refer to address and number below.
NHS: Director, National Medical Laser Centre,
Rayne Institute, 5 University Street, London WC1E 6JJ.
Tel: 071 380 9801. Fax: 071 377 1710.

ACADEMIC: *Professor of Laser Medicine and Surgery,*
University College Hospital. DISTINCTIONS: *Editor,* Lasers in
Medical Science; *lately President, British Medical Laser*
Association. MAJOR DEGREES: *MD, FRCP. First qualified in*
Cambridge in 1971. Specialist training at University College
Hospital. USA: *AM (Harvard).*

CICLITIRA, Dr Paul J.

Coeliac disease.
PRIVATE: 12 St Ann's Road, London W11 4SR
Tel: 071 603 5321 Fax: 071 928 7965
NHS AND ACADEMIC: Senior Lecturer in Cellular and
Molecular Medicine, Gastro-enterology Unit, Rayne Institute,
St Thomas's Hospital, London, SE1 7EH.
Tel: 071 928 9292. Fax: 071 928 7965.

DISTINCTIONS: *British Gastroenterology Research Medal 1986;*
European Gastroenterology Award 1988. Editor, standard
work on molecular biology in gastroenterology. MAJOR
DEGREES: *MD, FRCP. First qualified in London in 1971.*
Specialist training at the Medical Research Council,
Cambridge, and St Bartholomew's Hospital.

DAWSON, Dr Anthony M.

PRIVATE: 149 Harley Street, London W1N 2DE.
Tel: 071 935 4444, Fax: 071 486 3782.
NHS: Retired.

DISTINCTIONS: *Physician to HM the Queen and Head of HMs Medical Household. Councillor, Royal College of Physicians.* MAJOR DEGREES: *MD, FRCS. First qualified in London in 1951. Specialist training at the Royal Free Hospital.*

DOWLING, Professor R. Hermon.

Especially gallstones.
PRIVATE: Refer to address and number below.
NHS AND ACADEMIC: Professor of Gastroenterology,
Guy's Hospital, St Thomas Street, London SE1 9RT.
Tel: 071 955 5000.

DISTINCTION: *President, European Society for Clinical Investigation.* MAJOR DEGREES: *MD, FRCP. First qualified in Belfast in 1968. USA: Lately Senior Research Fellow, Boston University.*

FARTHING, Professor Michael J. G.

Especially infections.
PRIVATE: Refer to address and number below.
NHS: Consultant Physician, Department of Gastroenterology,
St Bartholomew's Hospital, West Smithfield,
London EC1A 7BE. Tel: 071 601 8888. Fax: 071 601 7899.

ACADEMIC: *Professor of Gastroenterology, St Bartholomew's.* MAJOR DEGREES: *MD, FRCP.First qualified in London in 1972. Specialist training at Cambridge and St Mark's Hospital. USA: Lately Assistant Professor in Medicine, Tufts University, Boston.*

FORGACS, Dr Ian C.

Especially gallbladders and bileducts.
PRIVATE. Refer to address and number below.
NHS: Consultant Gastroenterologist, King's College Hospital, Denmark Hill, London SE5 9RS.
Tel: 071 274 6222. Fax: 071 326 3438.

MAJOR DEGREES: MD, MRCP. First qualified in London in 1975. Specialist training at St Thomas's Hospital, and Addenbrooke's Hospital, Cambridge.

HATFIELD, Dr Adrian R. W.

Gallbladders and bileducts.
PRIVATE: 18 Upper Wimpole Street, London W1M 7TB.
Tel: 071 224 4598.
NHS: Consultant Gastroenterologist, Middlesex Hospital, Mortimer Street, London W1N 8AA.
Tel: 071 636 8333. Fax: 071 323 0397.

MAJOR DEGREES: MD, FRCP. First qualified in London in 1969. Specialist training at the Royal London Hospital.

MISIEWICZ, Dr Jerzy J. (George)

Especially treatment of hollow organs.
PRIVATE: 148 Harley Street, London W1N 1AH.
Tel: 071 935 1207. Fax: 071 224 1528.
NHS: Consultant Gastroenterologist, Central Middlesex Hospital, Acton Lane, Park Royal, London NW10 7NS.
Tel: 081 965 5733.

DISTINCTIONS: Consultant Gastroenterologist to the Royal Navy; Editor, European Journal of Gastroenterology and Hepatology; Councillor, British Society of Gastroenterology. MAJOR DEGREE: FRCP. First qualified in London in 1956.

Specialist training at the Royal Postgraduate Medical School and St Bartholomew's Hospital.

POUNDER, Dr Roy E.

PRIVATE: See address and number below.
NHS AND ACADEMIC: Reader, Royal Free Hospital, Pond Street, London NW3 2QG. Tel: 071 794 0500. Fax: 971 435 5342.

MAJOR DEGREES: MD, FRCP. First qualified in Cambridge in 1970. Specialist training at St Thomas's Hospital.

SILK, Dr David B.

Including upper endoscopy and liver complaints.
Private: 55 Harley Street, London W1N 1DD.
Tel: 071 631 1595.
NHS: Consultant Physician, Central Middlesex Hospital, Acton Lane, Park Royal, London NW10 7NS.
Tel: 081 965 5733.

MAJOR DEGREES: MD, FRCP. First qualified in London in 1968. Specialist training at King's College Hospital, London. USA: Lately Associate Professor, University of California.

SWAIN, Dr C. Paul.

Especially laser treatments.
Private: Refer to address and number below.
NHS: Consultant Gastroenterologist, Royal London Hospital, Whitechapel Road, London E1 1BB.
Tel: 071 377 7000. Fax: 071 377 7396 or 7122.

MAJOR DEGREES: MD, FRCP. First qualified in London in 1972. Specialist training at St Bartholomew's and the Royal London Hospitals.

GENERAL SURGEONS

ALLUM, Mr William H.

PRIVATE: Refer to address and number below.
NHS: Consultant Surgeon, St Bartholomew's Hospital,
West Smithfield, London EC1A 7BE.
Tel: 071 601 8888. Fax: 071 601 7899.

DISTINCTION: *Secretary, British Stomach Cancer Group.*
MAJOR DEGREES: *MD, FRCS. First qualified in Birmingham in
1977. Specialist training in Birmingham and Leicester.*
USA: *MD, Oncology Unit, University of Houston, Texas.*

CHALSTREY, Mr Leonard J.

PRIVATE: 116 Harley Street, London W1N 1AG.
Tel: 071 935 7413.
NHS: Consultant Surgeon, St Bartholomew's Hospital,
West Smithfield, London EC1A 7BE.
Tel: 071 601 8888. Fax: 071 601 7899.

ACADEMIC: *Senior Lecturer in Surgery, St Bartholomew's.*
MAJOR DEGREES: *MD, FRCS. First qualified in Cambridge in
1957. Specialist training at St Bartholomew's and the Royal
Free Hospitals.*

COCHRANE, Mr John P. S.

PRIVATE: 19 Wimpole Street, London W1M 7AD.
Tel: 071 637 9755.
NHS: Consultant Surgeon, Whittington Hospital,
Highgate Hill, London N19 5NT.
Tel: 071 272 3070. Fax: 071 272 6819.

MAJOR DEGREES. *MS, FRCS. First qualified in London in
1967. Specialist training at Leicester and the Middlesex
Hospital.*

EARLAM, Mr Richard J.

PRIVATE: 55 Harley Street, London W1N 1DD.
Tel: 071 637 4288.
NHS: Consultant Surgeon, Royal London Hospital,
Whitechapel, London E1 1BB.
Tel: 071 377 7000. Fax: 071 377 7396 or 7122.

DISTINCTIONS: *Examiner, Royal College of Surgeons;
Chairman, International Society of Gastric Surgery.* MAJOR
DEGREES: *MChir, FRCS. First qualified in Cambridge in 1958.
Specialist training at the Liverpool Royal Infirmary and in
Munich, Germany. USA: Lately Research Assistant,
the Mayo Clinic.*

HABIBI, Mr Magi.

PRIVATE: Refer to address and number below.
NHS: Consultant Surgeon, Hammersmith Hospital,
150 Du Cane Road, London W12 0HS.
Tel: 081 743 2030. Fax: 081 740 3169.

MAJOR DEGREES: *MS, FRCS. First qualified in London in
1978. Specialist training at the Royal Postgraduate Medical
School.*

JACKSON, Mr Barry T.

PRIVATE: York House, 199 Westminster Bridge Road,
London SE1 7UT. Tel: 071 928 5485. Fax: 071 928 3748.
NHS: Consultant Surgeon, St Thomas's Hospital,
Lambeth Palace Road, London SE1 7EH.
Tel: 071 928 9292. Fax: 071 922 8079.

DISTINCTIONS: *Surgeon to HM the Queen; lately Examiner
and Arris and Gale Lecturer, Royal College of Surgeons.*
MAJOR DEGREES: *MS, FRCS. First qualified in London in
1963. Specialist training at St Thomas's Hospital.*

KIRKHAM, Mr John S.

PRIVATE: 149 Harley Street, London W1N 2DE.
Tel: 071 935 4444. Fax: 071 486 3782.
NHS: Consultant Surgeon, Queen Mary's Hospital,
Roehampton, London SW15 5PN. Tel: 081 789 6611.

DISTINCTIONS: *Examiner, Royal College of Surgeons,
Edinburgh.* MAJOR DEGREE: *FRCS. First qualified in 1961.*

McCOLL, Professor Rt. Hon. Lord

PRIVATE: Refer to address and number below.
NHS: Director of Surgery, Guy's Hospital, St Thomas Street
London SE1 9RT. Tel: 071 955 5000.

ACADEMIC: *Professor of Surgery, Guy's and St Thomas's
United Medical Schools.* DISTINCTIONS: *Consultant Surgeon to
the Army; Honorary Surgeon, King's College; Adviser on
Medical Features, BBC TV; Councillor, Royal College of
Surgeons and the Imperial Cancer Research Fund.* MAJOR
DEGREES: *FRCS, FACS. First qualified in London in 1957.*
USA: *Research Fellow, Harvard.*

MENZIES-GOW, Mr Neil.

*Especially minimally invasive (laparoscopic) surgery of the
abdomen, appendix, gall bladder etc.*
PRIVATE: Princess Grace Hospital, 42/52 Nottingham Place,
London W1M 3FD. Tel: 071 486 1234.
NHS: Consultant, Central Middlesex Hospital, Acton Lane,
Park Royal, London NW10 7NS. Tel: 081 965 5733.

ACADEMIC: *Senior Lecturer, Middlesex Hospital Medical
School, London.* MAJOR DEGREE: *FRCS. First qualified in
London in 1969.*

ROSIN, Mr R. David.

Minimally invasive surgery.
PRIVATE: 6 Harley Street, London W1N 1AA.
Tel: 071 631 3447. Fax: 071 631 3459.
NHS: Consultant Surgeon, St Mary's Hospital, Praed Street,
London W2 1NY. Tel: 071 262 1280. Fax: 071 725 6200.

DISTINCTIONS: *Lately Arris and Gale Lecturer, Arnott Lecturer
and Penrose May Tutor, Royal College of Surgeons;
Examiner, RCS, Edinburgh; President, Melinoma Study
Group.* MAJOR DEGREES: *FRCS, MS. First qualified in London
in 1966. Specialist training at the Westminster Hospital.*

SCURR , Mr John H.

PRIVATE: 5 Baniel Gate, London SW1V 3SD.
Tel: 071 834 5578. Fax: 071 834 6315.
NHS AND ACADEMIC: Senior Lecturer and Consultant Surgeon,
Middlesex Hospital, Mortimer Street, London W1N 8AA.
Tel: 071 636 8333. Fax: 071 323 0397.

MAJOR DEGREE: *FRCS. First qualified in London in 1972.
Specialist training at the Middlesex and Westminster
Hospitals.*

THOMAS, Mr J. Merion.

PRIVATE: The Lister Hospital, Chelsea Bridge Road,
London SW1W 8RH. Tel: 071 259 9552.
NHS : Consultant Surgeon Oncologist, Chelsea and
Westminster Hospital, 369 Fulham Road,
London SW10 9NH. Tel: 081 746 8000. Fax: 081 746 8111.

MAJOR DEGREE: MS, FRCS. First qualified in London in 1969.
Specialist training at the Royal Marsden and St Mark's
Hospitals.

WASTELL, Professor Christopher.

Especially laparoscopic (minimally invasive) surgery.
PRIVATE: Refer to address and number below.
NHS AND ACADEMIC: Professor of Gastroenterological Surgery,
Chelsea and Westminster Hospital, 369 Fulham Road,
London SW10 9NH. Tel: 081 746 8000. Fax: 081 746 8111.

DISTINCTIONS: Examiner, Royal College of Surgeons. President
of the Huntington Society. MAJOR DEGREES: MS, FRCS. First
qualified in London in 1957. Specialist training at the
Westminster Hospital. USA: Lately Research Fellow in
Surgery, Mount Sinai Medical Center, New York.

WELLWOOD, Mr James.

Minimally invasive (laparoscopic) surgery of the abdomen,
appendix, gallbladder etc.
PRIVATE: 134 Harley Street, London W1N 3AH.
Tel: 071 487 4212. Fax: 071 486 1042
NHS: Consultant Surgeon, Whipp's Cross Hospital,
Whipp's Cross Road, Leytonstone, London E11 1NR.
Tel: 081 539 5522.

ACADEMIC: Lecturer, St Bartholomew's Medical College.
DISTINCTIONS: Queen's Commendation, 1971; Honorary
Secretary, British Association of Surgical Oncology. MAJOR
DEGREES: FRCS, MChir. First qualified in Cambridge in 1966.
Specialist training and research at St Bartholomew's and
St Thomas's Hospitals.

GENITO-URINARY PHYSICIANS

BARNES, Dr Simon E.

Especially sexually-transmitted diseases in women.
Private: refer to address and number below.
NHS: Consultant in Genito-Urinary Medicine,
Charing Cross Hospital, Fulham Palace Road,
London W6 8RF. Tel: 081 846 1234. Fax: 081 846 1111.

MAJOR DEGREES: MD, MRCOG. First qualified in London in
1982. Specialist training at Westminster and St Stephen's
Hospitals.

BINGHAM, Dr James S.

PRIVATE: 59 Park Road, London. W4 3EY. Tel: 071 254 4499.
NHS: Consultant-in-Charge, Genito-Urinary Medicine,
St Thomas's Hospital, Lambeth Palace Road,
London SE1 7EH. Tel 071 928 9292. Fax: 071 922 8079.

MAJOR DEGREE: FRCOG. First qualified in Belfast in 1969.
Specialist training at the Middlesex Hospital and in
Vancouver, Canada.

BOWAG, Dr Fiona C.

Especially sexually transmitted diseases in women.
PRIVATE: Refer to address and number below.
NHS: Consultant in Genito-Urinary Medicine,
Chelsea and Westminster Hospital, 369 Fulham Road,
London SW10 9NH. Tel: 081 746 8000. Fax: 081 746 8111.

MAJOR DEGREE: MRCP. First qualified in London in 1980.
Specialist training at the Royal Free and University College
Hospitals.

BRADBEER, Dr Caroline S.

Especially diseases of prostitutes, including AIDS.
PRIVATE: Refer to address and number below.
NHS: Consultant in Genito-Urinary Medicine,
St Thomas's Hospital, Lambeth Palace Road,
London SE1 7EH. Tel: 071 928 9292. Fax: 071 922 8079.

MAJOR DEGREE: FRCP. First qualified in London in 1979.
Specialist training at St Thomas's.

EVANS, Dr Brian A.

PRIVATE: refer to address and number below.
NHS : Director, Genito-Urinary Medicine Clinic, Charing
Cross Hospital, Fulham Palace Road, London W6 8RF.
Tel: 081 748 2040.

DISTINCTION: Lately, President of the Medical Society for VD.
MAJOR DEGREE: FRCP. First qualified in London in 1959.
Specialist training at the Middlesex Hospital.

HARRIS, Dr John W.

Especially syphilis, including homosexual complications.
Private: 86 Harley Street, London W1N 1AE.
Tel: 071 486 4166.
NHS: Consultant in Venereology and Genito-Urinary
Medicine, St Mary's Hospital, Praed Street, London W2 1NY.
Tel: 071 262 1280 or 725 6666. Fax: 071 725 6200.

MAJOR DEGREE: FRCP. First qualified in Belfast in 1967.
Specialist training at King's College Hospital. USA: Visiting
Consultant, VD Control Center, Atlanta, Georgia.

HAWKINS, Dr David A.

PRIVATE: Refer to address and number below.
NHS: Consultant in Genito-Urinary Medicine,
Chelsea and Westminster Hospital, 369 Fulham Road,
London SW10 9NH.
Tel: 081 746 8000. Fax: 081 746 8111.

*MAJOR DEGREE: MRCP. First qualified in London in 1977.
Specialist training at Northwick Park and St Mary's Hospital.*

LIM, Dr Frederick T. K. S.

Including sexually transmitted hepatitis.
PRIVATE: Flat 6, 26 Devonshire Place, London W1N 1PD.
Tel: 071 224 1784. Fax: 071 224 1784.

*DISTINCTION: Lately, Consultant in Genito-Urinary Medicine,
King's College Hospital. MAJOR DEGREE: MRCP. First qualified in London in 1971. Specialist training at the Middlesex
and Charing Cross Hospitals.*

McMANUS, Dr Thomas G.

PRIVATE: Refer to address and number below.
NHS: Consultant Genito-Urinary Physician,
King's College Hospital, Denmark Hill, London SE5 9RS. Tel:
071 274 6222.

*MAJOR DEGREES: MRCOG, FRCP. First qualified in Glasgow
in 1972.*

SAMARASINGHE, Dr Priya L.

PRIVATE: Refer to address and number below.
NHS: Consultant in Genito-Urinary Medicine, Chelsea and
Westminster Hospital, 369 Fulham Road, London SW10 9N.
Tel: 081 746 8000. Fax: 081 746 8111.

*MAJOR DEGREE: FRCS. First qualified in Colombo, Sri Lanka
in 1962. Specialist training at Charing Cross Hospital.*

SIMMONS, Dr Paul D.

Especially hepatitis B in homosexuals.
PRIVATE: Refer to address and number below.
NHS: Consultant Genito-Urinary Physician,
St Bartholomew's Hospital, West Smithfield,
London EC1 7BE. Tel: 071 601 8888. Fax: 071 601 7899.

*DISTINCTION: Patron, Society of Health Advisers in Sexually
Transmitted Diseases. MAJOR DEGREE: FRCP. First qualified in
Leeds in 1971. Specialist training at St Bartholomew's and
St Thomas's Hospitals.*

SYMONDS, Dr Michael A. E.

PRIVATE: 138 Harley Street, London W1N 1AH.
Tel: 071 486 3979.
NHS: Consultant in Genito-Urinary Medicine,
St Bartholomew's Hospital, West Smithfield,
London EC1A 7BE. Tel: 071 601 8888. Fax: 071 601 7899.

*MAJOR DEGREE: FRCP. First qualified in London in 1958.
Specialist training at St Thomas's and King's College
Hospitals.*

WELCH, Dr Janet M.

PRIVATE: Refer to address and number below.
NHS: Consultant in Genito-Urinary Medicine,
King's College Hospital, Denmark Hill, London SE5 9RS.
Tel: 071 274 6222.

MAJOR DEGREE: MRCP. First qualified in London in 1980.
Specialist training at St Thomas's Hospital.

GERIATRICIANS

BEYNON, Dr Gareth P. J.

PRIVATE: Private Consulting Rooms, Woolavington Wing,
Middlesex Hospital, Cleveland Street, London W1N 8AA.
Tel (appointments): 081 445 5683.
Tel (hospital): 071 380 9022.
NHS: None.

MAJOR DEGREE: FRCP. *First qualified in Cambridge in 1964.*
Specialist training at the Middlesex Hospital.

CROKER, Dr John.

PRIVATE: 152 Harley Street, London W1N 1HH.
Tel: 071 935 8868.
NHS: Consultant Geriatrician, Middlesex Hospital,
Mortimer Street, London W1N 8AA.
Tel: 071 636 8333. Fax: 071 323 0387.

ACADEMIC: *Senior Lecturer, University College and Middlesex*
School of Medicine. MAJOR DEGREE: FRCP. *First qualified in*
Oxford in 1970. Specialist training at St Thomas's and the
Middlesex Hospitals.

HARRINGTON, Dr Mary G.

PRIVATE: Refer to address and number below.
NHS: Consultant Physician, Department of Geriatric
Medicine, King's College Hospital, Denmark Hill,
London SE5 9RS. Tel: 071 274 6222. Fax: 071 326 3589.

ACADEMIC: *Sub-Dean, King's College Medical School.* MAJOR
DEGREE: FRCP. *First qualified in London in 1976. Specialist*
training at the Middlesex Hospital and the Royal Postgraduate
Medical School.

HAEMATOLOGISTS

LEE, Dr Christine A.

Haemophilia.
PRIVATE: Refer to address and numbers below.
NHS: Consultant Haematologist, Haemophilia Unit,
Royal Free Hospital, Pond Street, London NW3 2QG.
Tel: 071 794 0500. Fax: 071 435 5342.

MAJOR DEGREES: MD, MRCPath, FRCP. First qualified in Oxford in 1969. Specialist training at the Royal Free and Charing Cross Hospitals.

MURPHY, Dr Michael F.

PRIVATE: Refer to address and number below.
NHS AND ACADEMIC: Senior Lecturer and Consultant
Haematologist, St Bartholomew's Hospital, West Smithfield,
London EC1A 7BE. Tel: 071 601 8888. Fax: 071 601 7899.

DISTINCTION: Secretary, British Committee for Standards in Haematology. MAJOR DEGREES: MD, MRCP, MRCPath. First qualified in London in 1973. Specialist training at St Barthlomew's Hospital.

WATERS, Professor Alan H.

Especially anaemia.
PRIVATE: Refer to address and number below.
NHS AND ACADEMIC: Professor of Haematology,
St Bartholomew's Hospital, West Smithfield,
London EC1A 7BE. Tel: 071 601 8888. Fax: 071 601 7899.

DISTINCTION: President, British Society for Haematology. Major degrees: MD, FRCP, FRCPath. First qualified (with honours) in Queensland, Australia in 1958. Specialist training in Melbourne, Australia and the Royal Postgraduate Medical School.

HEART SURGEONS

de LEVAL, Mr Marc R.

Doyen of children's heart surgery.
PRIVATE: Harley Street Clinic, 35 Weymouth Street,
London W1N 4BJ. Tel: 071 935 7700.
NHS: Consultant Cardiothoracic Surgeon, Hospital for Sick
Children, 34 Great Ormond Street, London WC1N 3JH.
Tel: 071 405 9200. Fax: 071 829 8643.

*MAJOR DEGREE: MD. First qualified in Liège, Belgium, in
1966.*

DEVERALL, Mr Philip B.

Adults and children.
PRIVATE: 21 Upper Wimpole Street, London W1M 7TA.
Tel: 071 486 7753.
NHS: Consultant Cardiothoracic Surgeon, Guy's Hospital,
St Thomas Street, London SE1 9RT.
Tel: 071 955 5000. Fax: 071 922 8079.

*ACADEMIC: Lecturer in Surgery, Guy's Hospital. MAJOR
DEGREE: FRCS. First qualified in London in 1960. Specialist
training at the Hospital for Sick Children, London. USA:
Cardiovascular Research Fellow, University of Alabama.*

EDMONDSON, Mr Stephen J.

PRIVATE: 69 Harley Street, London W1N 1DE.
Tel: 071 935 6375
NHS: Consultant Cardiothoracic Surgeon,
St Bartholomew's Hospital, West Smithfield,
London EC1A 7BE. Tel: 071 601 7130. Fax: 071 601 7899.

*MAJOR DEGREES: FRCS, FRCP. First qualified (with honours)
in London in 1974.*

LEWIS, Mr C. Terence.

PRIVATE: Cromwell Hospital, Cromwell Road,
London SW5 0TU. Tel: 071 370 4233. Fax: 071 370 4063.
NHS: Consultant Cardiothoracic Surgeon,
Royal London Hospital, Whitechapel, London E1 1BB.
Tel: 071 377 7000. Fax: 071 377 7396 or 7122

*MAJOR DEGREE: FRCS. First qualified in London in 1968.
Specialist training at the Royal Brompton and National Heart
and Royal London Hospitals.*

LINCOLN, Mr J. Christopher

Especially children.
PRIVATE: 38 Devonshire Street, London W1N 1LD.
Tel: 071 352 6086.
NHS: Consultant Cardiothoracic Surgeon,
Royal Brompton National Heart and Lung Hospital,
Fulham Road, London SW3 6HP.
Tel: 071 352 8121. Fax 071 351 8099.

*ACADEMIC: Senior Lecturer in Paediatric Surgery, Heart and
Lung Institute. DISTINCTION: Lately Hunterian Professor,
Royal College of Surgeons. MAJOR DEGREE: FRCS. First quali-
fied in Dublin in 1959. Specialist training at Great Ormond
Street and Westminster Hospitals. USA: Lately Clinical and
Research Fellow, Harvard Medical School and Massachusetts
General Hospital.*

PARKER, Mr D. John.

PRIVATE: 6 Upper Wimpole Street, London W1M 7TD.
Tel: 071 935 1590.
NHS: Consultant Cardiac Surgeon, St George's Hospital,
Blackshaw Road, London SW17 0QT. Tel: 081 672 1255.

ACADEMIC: Senior Lecturer, Heart and Lung Institute. MAJOR DEGREES: FRCS, FRCP. First qualified in St Andrews in 1962. Specialist training at Dundee Royal Infirmary and the National Heart Hospital.

REES, Mr Gareth M.

PRIVATE: 10 Upper Wimpole Street, London W1M 7TD.
Tel: 071 935 3922.
NHS: Cardiothoracic Surgeon in Charge,
St Bartholomew's Hospital, West Smithfield,
London EC1A 7BE. Tel: 071 601 4488. Fax: 071 601 7899.

ACADEMIC: Recognised Teacher, University of London. MAJOR DEGREES: FRCS, FRCP, MS. First qualified (with honours) in London in 1960. Specialist training at the Royal Brompton and National Heart Hospitals. USA: Lately Research Fellow in Cardiac Surgery, University of Oregon at Portland. Worked with Dr Albert Starr on the origin and development of bypass surgery.

SHABBO, Mr Fikrat

PRIVATE: Emblem House, London Bridge Hospital,
27 Tooley Street, London SE1 2PR.
Tel: 071 403 4884. Fax: 071 407 3162.
NHS: Consultant Cardiothoracic Surgeon, Brook Hospital,
Shooters Hill Road, London SE18 4LW. Tel: 081 856 5555.

MAJOR DEGREE: FRCS. Specialist training at the National Heart and St Bartholomew's Hospitals.

SMITH, Mr Peter A. J.

Especially bypass surgery.
PRIVATE: Refer to address and number below.
NHS: Consultant Cardiothoracic Surgeon,
Hammersmith Hospital, Du Cane Road, London W12 0HS.
Tel: 081 740 3125. Fax: 081 740 3179.

DISTINCTION: *Lately Hunterian Professor, Royal College of Surgeons.* MAJOR DEGREES: *MRCP, FRCS. First qualified in London in 1975. Specialist training at the Royal Brompton, Harefield and Middlesex Hospitals.*

STANBRIDGE, Mr Rex D. L.

NHS: Consultant Cardiothoracic Surgeon, St Mary's Hospital,
Praed Street, London W2 1NY.
Tel: 071 725 1241. Fax: 071 725 6200.

ACADEMIC: *Senior Lecturer, Royal Postgraduate Medical School.* MAJOR DEGREE: *FRCS. First qualified in London in 1971. Specialist training at Harefield and Hammersmith Hospitals.*

TAYLOR, Professor Kenneth M.

PRIVATE: Refer to address and number below.
NHS AND ACADEMIC: Professor of Cardiac Surgery,
Royal Postgraduate Medical School, Hammersmith Hospital,
150 Du Cane Road, London W12 0HS.
Tel: 081 743 2030. Fax: 081 740 3169.

MAJOR DEGREES: *MD, FRCS. First qualified in Glasgow in 1970. Specialist training at Glasgow University and Hammersmith Hospital.*

TREASURE, Mr Tom.

PRIVATE: 19 Wimpole Street, London W1M 7AD.
Tel: 071 637 9050.
NHS: Consultant Cardiothoracic Surgeon,
St George's Hospital, Blackshaw Road, London SW17 0QT.
Tel: 081 767 9859.

MAJOR DEGREES: MD, MS, FRCS. First qualified in London in 1970. Specialist training at the Royal Brompton and National Heart, Guy's and St Thomas's Hospitals.

WALESBY, Mr Robin K.

PRIVATE: 34 Devonshire Place, London W1N 1PE.
Tel: 071 486 4617.
NHS: Consultant Cardiothoracic Surgeon,
Royal Free Hospital, Pond Street, London NW3 2QG.
Tel: 071 794 0500. Fax: 071 435 5342.

ACADEMIC: Senior Lecturer, Heart and Lung Institute. MAJOR DEGREE: FRCS. First qualified in London in 1970. Specialist training at Harefield and the Middlesex Hospitals.

WILLIAMS, Mr Bryn T.

PRIVATE: Emblem House, London Bridge Hospital,
27 Tooley Street, London SE1 2PR.
Tel: 071 403 4884. Fax: 071 407 3162.
NHS: Consultant Cardiothoracic Surgeon,
St Thomas's Hospital, Lambeth Palace Road,
London SE1 7EH. Tel: 071 928 9292. Fax: 071 922 8079.

DISTINCTION: Consultant Cardiothoracic Surgeon to the Army. MAJOR DEGREE: FRCS. First qualified in Birmingham in 1962. USA: Fellow in Surgical Research, New York University, Buffalo.

WRIGHT, Mr John E. C.

PRIVATE: London Heart Clinic, 22 Upper Wimpole Street,
London W1M 7DG. Tel: 071 486 8961.
NHS: Consultant Cardiothoracic Surgeon,
London Chest Hospital, Bonner Road, London E2 9JS
Tel: 071 980 4433.

*MAJOR DEGREE: FRCS. First qualified in London in 1958.
Specialist training at the National Heart Hospital.
USA: Lately Research Fellow, Harvard Medical School and
Massachusetts General Hospital, Boston.*

WOOD, Mr Alan J.

PRIVATE: London Independent Hospital, Beaumont Square,
London E1. Tel: 071 791 2200. Fax: 071 265 9032.
NHS: Consultant Cardiothoracic Surgeon,
Royal London Hospital, Whitechapel, London E1 1BB.
Tel: 071 377 7151. Fax: 071 377 7396 or 7122.

*MAJOR DEGREE: FRCS. First qualified in London in 1975.
Specialist training at St Bartholomew's Hospital.*

YACOUB, Professor Sir Magdi.

Especially transplants.
PRIVATE: 24 Upper Wimpole Street, London W1M 7TA.
Tel: 071 935 6223.
NHS: Professor of Cardiac Surgery, Royal Brompton National
Heart and Lung Hospital, Fulham Road, London SW3 6HP.
Tel: 071 352 8121. Fax: 071 351 8099.

*MAJOR DEGREES: FRCS, FRCP. First qualified in London in
1966. USA: Department of Cardiothoracic Surgery,
University of Chicago.*

HEPATOBILIARY (LIVER) SUR

BENJAMIN, Professor Irving.

PRIVATE: Refer to address and number below.
NHS: Consultant Surgeon, King's College Hospital,
Denmark Hill, London SE5 9RS.
Tel: 071 274 6222. Fax: 071 326 3438

ACADEMIC: *Professor of Surgery, King's College. MAJOR
DEGREES: MD, FRCS. First qualified in Glasgow in 1971.
Specialist training at Groote Schuur Hospital, Cape Town,
South Africa; in Glasgow; and at the Royal Postgraduate
Medical School.*

RUSSELL, Mr R. Christopher.

PRIVATE: 149 Harley Street, London W1N 1HG.
Tel: 071 486 1164. Fax: 071 487 5997.
NHS: Consultant Surgeon, Middlesex Hospital,
Mortimer Street, London W1N 8AA.
Tel: 071 636 8333. Fax: 071 323 0397.

MAJOR DEGREES: *MS, FRCS. First qualified in London in
1963. Specialist training at St Mary's and Central Middlesex
Hospitals.*

WILLIAMSON, Professor Robin C. P.

PRIVATE: Refer to address and number below.
NHS: Director and Professor of Surgery,
Royal Postgraduate Medical School, Hammersmith Hospital,
150 Du Cane Road, London W12 0HS.
Tel: 081 740 3210. Fax: 081 740 3179.

DISTINCTIONS: *Research Medal, British Society of
Gastroenterology; lately Hallett Prize, Hunterian Professor
and Arris and Gale Lecturer, Royal College of Surgeons.*

Academic: Lately Professor of Surgery, Bristol University.
MAJOR DEGREES: *MD, MChir, FRCS. First qualified (with first-class honours) in Cambridge in 1968. Specialist training at United Hospitals, Bristol. USA: Lately Fulbright Fellow, Harvard and Massachusetts General Hospital.*

HEPATOLOGISTS (LIVER PHYSICIANS)

BURROUGHS, Dr Andrew K.

PRIVATE: Refer to address and number below.
NHS: Consultant Physician, Hepato-Bilary and Liver
Transplantation Unit, Royal Free Hospital, Pond Street,
London, NW3 3QG. Tel: 071 794 0500. Fax: 071 435 5342.

ACADEMIC: *Senior Lecturer, Royal Free Hospital.*
DISTINCTIONS: *Councillor, British Association for the Study of
the Liver, British Society of Gastroenterology.* MAJOR
DEGREES: *MD, FRCS. First qualified in Liverpool in 1976.*

MAXWELL, Dr J. Douglas.

PRIVATE: Refer to address and number below.
NHS: Consultant Physician, St George's Hospital,
Blackshaw Road, London SW17 0QT. Tel: 081 672 1255.

ACADEMIC: *Clinical Sub-Dean, St George's Hospital Medical
School.* MAJOR DEGREES: *MD, FRCP. First qualified in
Glasgow in 1964. Specialist training at King's College and
St George's Hospitals.* USA: *Lately Research Fellow,
University of California Medical School, San Francisco.*

MURRAY-LYON, Dr Iain M.

PRIVATE: 6 Devonshire Place, London W1N 1HH.
Tel: 071 935 6747.
NHS: Consultant Physician, Department of Gastroenterology,
Chelsea and Westminster Hospital, 369 Fulham Palace Road,
London SW10 9NH. Tel: 081 746 8000. Fax: 081 746 8111.

MAJOR DEGREES: *MD, FRCP. First qualified (with honours) in
Edinburgh in 1964. Specialist training at the Royal Infirmary,
Edinburgh, and the Liver Unit, King's College Hospital.*

THOMAS, Professor Howard C.

Especially hepatitis B.
PRIVATE: Refer to address and number below.
NHS: Consultant Physician and Director, Hepatology Unit,
St Mary's Hospital, Praed Street, London W2 1PG.
Tel: 071 725 1606. Fax: 071 725 6200.

ACADEMIC: *Professor of Medicine, St Mary's.* DISTINCTION:
Councillor, European Association for the Study of the Liver.
MAJOR DEGREE: *PhD, FRCP, FRCPS, MRCPath. First qualified in Newcastle in 1969. Specialist training in Glasgow and
at the Royal Free Hospital.*

WESTABY, Dr David.

Endoscopic investigation.
PRIVATE: Cromwell Hospital, Cromwell Road,
London SW5 0TU. Tel: 071 370 4233. Fax: 071 370 4063.
NHS: Consultant Physician, Liver Unit, Chelsea and
Westminster Hospital, 369 Fulham Road,
London SW10 9NH. Tel: 081 746 8000. Fax: 081 746 8111.

MAJOR DEGREE: *FRCP. First qualified in Cambridge in 1976.
Specialist training at King's College Hospital.*

WILLIAMS, Dr Roger.

PRIVATE: Private Wing, King's College Hospital.
NHS: Director, Liver Unit, King's College Hospital,
Denmark Hill, London SE5 9RS.
Tel: 071 274 6222. Fax: 071 326 3589.

DISTINCTIONS: *Consultant to the Army and the Liver Research
Unit Trust.* MAJOR DEGREES: *MD, FRCP, FRCS. First qualified
in London in 1953. Specialist training at the Royal Free*

*Hospital. USA: Lately Fellow, Columbia Presbyterian
Hospital, New York.*

ZEEGEN, Dr Ronald.

PRIVATE: Lister Hospital, Chelsea Bridge Road,
London SW1W 8RH. Tel: 071 730 3417. Fax: 071 824 8867.
NHS: Consultant Physician, Chelsea and Westminster
Hospital, 369 Fulham Road, London SW10 9NH.
Tel: 081 746 8000. Fax: 081 746 8111.

MAJOR DEGREE: FRCP. *First qualified in London in 1962.
Specialist training at Westminster and St Bartholomew's
Hospitals.*

HIV/AIDS PHYSICIANS

ADLER, Professor Michael W.

PRIVATE: Refer to address and number below.
NHS AND ACADEMIC: Professor of Genito-Urinary Medicine,
James Pringle House, Middlesex Hospital, London W1N 8AA.
Tel: 071 380 9146.

MAJOR DEGREES: *MD, FFCM, FRCP. First qualified in London
in 1965. Specialist training at St Thomas's Hospital.*

GAZZARD, Dr Brian G.

PRIVATE: 138 Harley Street, London W1N 1AH.
Tel: 071 935 0554.
NHS: Consultant Physician, Chelsea and Westminster
Hospital, 369 Fulham Road, London SW10 9NH.
Tel: 081 746 8000. Fax: 081 746 8111.

MAJOR DEGREES: *MD, FRCP. First qualified (with honours) in
Cambridge in 1971. Specialist training at St Bartholomew's
and King's College Hospitals.*

JOHNSON, Dr Margaret.

Including women.
PRIVATE: Refer to address and number below.
NHS: Consultant Physician in Charge, HIV/AIDS Clinic,
Royal Free Hospital, Pond Street, London NW3 2QG.
Tel: 071 794 0550. Fax: 071 435 5342.

MAJOR DEGREES: *MD, MRCP. First qualified in London in
1975. Specialist training at the Royal Brompton and Royal
Free Hospitals.*

PINCHING, Professor Anthony J.

PRIVATE: Refer to address and number below.
NHS AND ACADEMIC: Professor of Genito-Urinary Medicine,
St Bartholomew's Hospital, West Smithfield,
London EC1A 7BE.
Tel: 071 601 8888. Fax: 071 601 7899.

MAJOR DEGREES: *DPhil, FRCP. First qualified in Oxford in
1973. Specialist training at the Royal Postgraduate Medical
School and St Mary's Hospital.*

POZNIAC, Dr Anton

PRIVATE: Refer to address and number below.
NHS: Consultant Physician, HIV/AIDS Clinic,
King's College Hospital, Denmark Hill, London SE5 9RS.
Tel: 071 274 6222.

MAJOR DEGREES: *MD, MRCP. First qualified in London.
Specialist training at the Middlesex and King's College
Hospitals.*

MEDICAL ONCOLOGISTS
(CANCER PHYSICIANS)

BAUM, Professor Michael.

Breast cancer.
Private: Refer to address and number below.
NHS AND ACADEMIC: Professor of Surgery,
Royal Marsden Hospital, Downs Road, Sutton, Surrey.
Tel: 081 642 6011. Fax: 081 643 0373.

DISTINCTIONS: Director, Cancer Research Campaign at
Clinical trials Centre; Honorary Doctorate, Gothenburg,
Sweden; previously Professor of Surgery at King's College.
MAJOR DEGREE: FRCS. First qualified in Birmingham in 1960.
Specialist training at the University of Wales. USA: Lately
Instructor in Surgery, Pittsburgh University, Pennsylvania.

COOMBES, Dr R. Charles.

Breast cancer.
Private: Refer to address and number below.
NHS: Consultant Physician,
Department of Medical Oncology, Charing Cross Hospital,
Fulham Palace Road, London W6 8RF.
Tel: 081 846 1234. Fax: 081 846 1111.

ACADEMIC: Senior Lecturer, Institute of Cancer Research;
Senior Clinical Scientist, Ludwig Institute of Cancer Research.
DISTINCTION: Honorary Consultant Physician, Royal Marsden
Hospital. MAJOR DEGREES: PhD, MD, FRCP. First qualified in
1971. Specialist training at the Institute of Cancer Research,
the Royal Marsden Hospital and the Royal Postgraduate
Medical School.

CUNNINGHAM, Dr David.

Gastric cancer and lymphoma.
PRIVATE: Refer to address and number below.
NHS: Consultant Physician, Royal Marsden Hospital,
Downs Road, Sutton, Surrey SN2 5PT.
Tel: 081 642 6011. Fax: 081 643 0373.

ACADEMIC: Senior Lecturer, Institute of Cancer Research.
MAJOR DEGREES: MD, FRCP. First qualified in Glasgow in
1978. Specialist training at St Mary's Hospital.

GILMORE, Mr O. Jeremy.

Breast cancer.
Private: 30 Harley Street, London W1N 1AB.
Tel: 071 637 8820. Fax: 071 436 2945.
NHS: Lately Director of St. Bartholemew's Breast Unit.

DISTINCTIONS: Lately Hunterian Professor, Royal College of
Surgeons; Moynihan Medal, US Association of Surgeons;
Hamilton Bailey Prize, International College of Surgeons.
MAJOR DEGREES: MS, FRCS. First qualified (with special
award) in London in 1966. Specialist training at
St Bartholomew's Hospital.

GOLDMAN, Professor John M.

Leukaemia.
PRIVATE: Refer to address and number below.
NHS: Director, Centre for Adult Leukaemia,
Hammersmith Hospital, 150 Du Cane Road,
London W12 OHS.
Tel: 081 743 2030. Fax: 081 740 3169.

ACADEMIC: Professor of Leukaemia Biology, Royal
Postgraduate Medical School. MAJOR DEGREES: DM, FRCP,

FRCPath. First qualified in London in 1963. Specialist training at St Bartholomew's and the Royal Postgraduate Medical School. USA: Lately Fellow in Medicine, University of Miami and Massachusetts General Hospital, Boston.

HARPER, Dr Peter G.

PRIVATE: 97 Harley Street, London W1N 1DE.
Tel: 071 935 6698. Fax: 071 224 6504.
NHS: Consultant Physician and Medical Oncologist,
Guy's Hospital, St Thomas Street, London SE1 9RT.
Tel: 071 955 5000.

ACADEMIC: Senior Lecturer, UDMS Guy's and St Thomas's. MAJOR DEGREE: FRCP. First qualified in London in 1970. Specialist training at University College and St Mary's Hospitals.

HOFFBRAND, Professor A. Victor.

Especially leukaemia and lymphoma.
PRIVATE: Refer to address and number below.
NHS: Consultant Physician, Royal Free Hospital,
Pond Street, London NW3 2QG.
Tel: 071 794 0500. Fax: 071 435 5342.

ACADEMIC: Professor of Haematology, Royal Free Hospital Medical School; previously Senior Lecturer, Royal Postgraduate Medical School. MAJOR DEGREES: DSc, DM, FRCPath. First qualified in Oxford in 1959. Specialist training at St Bartholomew's Hospital and the Royal Postgraduate Medical School.

MALPAS, Professor James S.

Children's cancer.
PRIVATE: Refer to address and number below.
NHS: Consultant Physician, St Bartholomew's Hospital,
West Smithfield, London EC1A 7BE.
Tel. 071 601 8888. Fax: 071 601 7899.

ACADEMIC: *Professor of Medical Oncology, Medical College of
St Bartholomew's.* DISTINCTIONS: *Examiner to the universities
of London and Oxford; Deputy Director, Imperial Cancer
Research Fund, London; Vice-President, St Bartholomew's
Hospital Medical College.* MAJOR DEGREES: *MD, FRCP. First
qualified in London in 1955. Specialist training at the
Radcliffe Infirmary, Oxford; the Royal Postgraduate Medical
School and St Bartholomew's.*

NEWLANDS, Professor Edward.

Brain tumours and testicular cancer.
PRIVATE: Refer to address and numbers below.
NHS: Consultant in Medical Oncology,
Charing Cross Hospital, Fulham Palace Road,
London W6 8RF. Tel: 081 846 1234. Fax: 081 846 1111.

ACADEMIC: *Professor of Medical Oncology, Charing Cross and
Westminster Medical School.* MAJOR DEGREES: *Phd, FRCP.
First qualified in Oxford in 1966. Specialist training at
Westminster and Charing Cross Hospitals.*

OLIVER, Professor R. Timothy.

Especially bladder, kidney and testicular cancer.
PRIVATE: Refer to address and number below.
NHS AND ACADEMIC: Professor of Medical Oncology,
Royal London Hospital, Whitechapel Road, London E1 1BB.
Tel: 071 377 7000. Fax: 071 377 7396 or 7122.

MAJOR DEGREES: *MD, FRCP. First qualified in London in 1966. Specialist training at the London and St Bartholomew's Hospitals.*

POWLES, Dr Ray L.

Leukaemia and lymphoma.
PRIVATE: Refer to address and number below.
NHS: Consultant Physician in Charge, Leukaemia Unit, Royal Marsden Hospital, Downs Road, Sutton, Surrey SN2 5PT. Tel: 081 642 6011. Fax: 081 770 7313.

DISTINCTIONS: *Member, Academic Board of the Institute of Cancer Research; Member, Medical Research Council and Government Working Party on Adult Leukaemia.* MAJOR DEGREES: *MD, FRCP. First qualified in 1964. Specialist training at St Bartholomew's Hospital.*

POWLES, Dr Trevor J.

Breast cancer.
PRIVATE: Refer to address and number below.
NHS: Consultant Medical Oncologist,
Royal Marsden Hospital, Downs Road, Sutton,
Surrey SN2 5PT. Tel: 081 642 6011. Fax: 081 643 0373.

DISTINCTION: *Chairman, Medical Division, Royal Marsden Hospital.* MAJOR DEGREES: *PhD, FRCP. First qualified in London in 1964. Specialist training at the Royal Postgraduate Medical School and the Royal Marsden Hospital.*

PRENTICE, Dr H. Grant.

Especially leukaemia and bone marrow transplants.
PRIVATE: Refer to address and number below.
NHS: Director, Bone Marrow Transplants Programme,
Royal Free Hospital, Pond Street, London NW3 2QG.
Tel: 071 794 0500. Fax: 071 435 5342.

ACADEMIC: *Senior Lecturer, Academic Department of
Haematology, Royal Free Hospital.* MAJOR DEGREES: *FRCP,
FRCPath. First qualified in London in 1968. Specialist train-
ing at St George's and the Royal Marsden Hospitals.*

RUSTIN, Dr Gordon J. S.

Tumours.
PRIVATE: Refer to address and number below.
NHS AND ACADEMIC: Senior Lecturer and Consultant
Physician, Charing Cross Hospital, Fulham Palace Road,
London W6 8RF. Tel: 081 846 1234. Fax: 081 846 1111.

MAJOR DEGREES: *MD, MRCP. First qualified in London in
1971. Specialist training at the Royal Postgraduate Medical
School.*

SIKORA, Professor Karol.

Investigational therapies, gene therapy.
PRIVATE: Refer to address and number below.
NHS: Director, Department of Clinical Oncology,
Hammersmith Hospital, 150 Du Cane Road,
London W12 0HS Tel: 081 740 3060. Fax: 081 740 3169.

ACADEMIC: *Professor of Clinical Oncology, Royal
Postgraduate Medical School.* DISTINCTION: *Twining Medal,
Royal College of Radiology.* MAJOR DEGREES: *PhD, FRCP,*

FRCR. *First qualified in Cambridge in 1973. Specialist training in Cambridge and at St Bartholomew's Hospital.*
USA: Lately Fellow in Medical Oncology, Stanford University Hospital, Palo Alto, California.

SLEVIN, Dr Maurice L.

Breast, colon and lung cancers.
PRIVATE: 134 Harley Street, London W1N 1AH.
Tel: 071 224 0685.
NHS: Consultant Physician, St Bartholomew's Hospital,
West Smithfield, London EC1A 7BE.
Tel: 071 601 8888. Fax: 071 601 7899.

MAJOR DEGREES: *MD, FRCP. First qualified in Cape Town, South Africa, in 1973. Specialist training at Groote Schuur Hospital, Cape Town, and St Bartholomew's Hospital.*

SMITH, Dr Ian E.

Breast cancer.
PRIVATE: Refer to address and number below.
NHS: Consultant Medical Oncologist,
Royal Marsden Hospital, Fulham Road, London SW3 6JJ.
Tel: 071 352 8171. Fax: 071 352 5441.

MAJOR DEGREES: *MD, FRCP. First qualified in Edinburgh in 1971. Specialist training at Edinburgh Royal Infirmary and the Royal Marsden Hospital. USA: Member, American Society of Medical Oncologists.*

SOUHAMI, Professor Robert L.

Bone and muscle tumours.
PRIVATE: Refer to address and number below.
NHS: Consultant Physician, University College Hospital,
Gower Street, London WC1E 6AU.
Tel: 071 387 9300. Fax: 071 380 9977.

*ACADEMIC: Professor of Clinical Oncology, University College
and Middlesex hospitals. DISTINCTIONS: Chairman,
Association of Cancer Physicians and of the Cancer Therapy
Committee of the Medical Research Council. MAJOR DEGREES:
MD, FRCP. First qualified in London in 1962. Specialist train-
ing at University College and St Mary's Hospital.*

WAXMAN, Dr Jonathan.

Cancer of the bladder, the kidney and the prostate.
PRIVATE: Refer to address and number below.
NHS: Consultant Physician, Hammersmith Hospital,
150 Du Cane Road, London W12 0HS.
Tel: 081 740 3060. Fax: 081 743 8766.

*ACADEMIC: Reader, Royal Postgraduate Medical School.
MAJOR DEGREES: MD, FRCP. First qualified in London in
1975. Specialist training at University College Hospital, and
Addenbrooke's Hospital, Cambridge.*

WRIGLEY, Dr Peter F. M.

Cancer of the intestine, the stomach and lymphomas.
PRIVATE: 134 Harley Street, London W1N 1DJ.
Tel: 071 487 3193. Fax: 071 487 3071.
NHS: Consultant Physician, Department of Medical
Oncology, St Bartholomew's Hospital, West Smithfield,
London EC1A 7BE. Tel: 071 601 8888. Fax: 071 601 7899.

ACADEMIC: *Lately Senior Lecturer in Medical Oncology, St Bartholomew's Hospital Medical College.* DISTINCTION: *Lately, Chairman, Medical Research Council's Gastric Cancer Group.* MAJOR DEGREES: *PhD, FRCP. First qualified in Oxford in 1964. Specialist training at the John Radcliffe Infirmary, Oxford.*

NEPHROLOGISTS (KIDNEY PHYSICIANS)

BAKER, Dr Lawrence R.

Especially stone diseases, chronic renal failure and dialysis.
PRIVATE: 149 Harley Street, London W1N 2DE.
Tel: 071 935 4444.
NHS: Director of Renal Medicine and Transplantation,
St Bartholomew's Hospital, West Smithfield,
London EC1A 7BE.
Tel (direct): 071 601 8787. Fax: 071 601 7899.

ACADEMIC: *Lately Research Fellow, St Mary's Hospital,
London.* DISTINCTIONS: *Examiner, Royal College of
Physicians; lately Postgraduate Dean, St Bartholomew's.*
MAJOR DEGREES: *MD, FRCP. First qualified in Cambridge in
1964. Specialist training at the Royal Postgraduate Medical
School and Westminster and St Mary's Hospitals.*

CUNNINGHAM, Dr John.

Especially in relation to bone disease.
PRIVATE: London Independent Hospital, 1 Beaumont Square,
London E1 4NL. Tel: 071 791 2200. Fax: 071 265 9032.
NHS: Consultant Physician and Nephrologist, Royal
London Hospital, Whitechapel Road, London E1 1BB.
Tel: 071 377 7000.

ACADEMIC: *Lately Lecturer, London Hospital.* MAJOR
DEGREES: *DM, FRCP. First qualified in Oxford in 1973.
Specialist training at the Royal London and Middlesex
Hospitals. USA: Lately Fellow in Metabolism, Washington
University, St Louis, Missouri.*

EISINGER, Dr Anthony J. M. F.

Especially dialysis.
PRIVATE: 54 Wimpole Street, London W1M 7DF.
Tel: 081 644 1168.
NHS: Director, South West Thames Regional Renal Unit,
St Helier Hospital, Carshalton, Surrey SM5 1AA.
Tel: 081 644 4343.

MAJOR DEGREE: *FRCP. First qualified (with honours) in Cambridge
in 1965. Specialist training at the Middlesex, Royal Brompton and
National Heart and St Thomas's Hospitals.*

HILTON, Dr Philip J.

PRIVATE: Private Consulting Rooms, St Thomas's Hospital,
Lambeth Palace Road, London SE1 7EH. Tel: 071 928 5485.
NHS: Consultant Physician, St Thomas's Hospital,
Lambeth Palace Road, London SE1 7EH.
Tel: 071 928 9292. Fax: 071 922 8079.

MAJOR DEGREES: *MD, FRCP. First qualified in Cambridge in
1963. Specialist training at Addenbrooke's Hospital,
Cambridge, and St Thomas's Hospital.*

JONES, Dr Norman F.

PRIVATE: Private Consulting Rooms, St Thomas's Hospital,
Lambeth Palace Road, London SE1 7EH.
Tel: 071 928 5485. Fax: 071 922 8079.
NHS: Consultant Physician, St Thomas's Hospital,
Lambeth Palace Road, London SE1 7EH.
Tel: 071 928 9292. Fax: 071 922 8079.

DISTINCTIONS: *Consultant to the Metropolitan Police and the
Royal Army Medical Corps.* MAJOR DEGREES: *MD, FRCP.
First qualified in Cambridge in 1956.*

MARSH, Dr Francis (Frank) P.

Especially dialysis.
Private: London Independent Hospital, 1 Beaumont Square,
London E1 4NL. Tel: 071 790 0990. Fax: 071 265 9032.
NHS: Consultant Physician, Royal London Hospital,
Whitechapel, London El lBB.
Tel: 071 377 7418. Fax: 071 377 7291.

*Academic: Dean of Medical Studies, Royal London Hospital
Medical College. Major degree: FRCP. First qualified in
Cambridge in 1960. Specialist training at the Royal London
Hospital.*

MOORHEAD, Dr John F.

Private: St John and Elizabeth Hospital, 60 Grove End Road,
Swiss Cottage, London NW8. Tel: 071 286 5126.
NHS: Director, Department of Nephrology and
Transplantation, Royal Free Hospital, Pond Street,
London NW3 2QG. Tel: 071 794 0500. Fax: 071 435 5342.

*Distinction: Examiner, University of London. Major
degree: FRCP. First qualified in Liverpool in 1957.*

NEILD, Professor Guy H.

Especially in connection with diabetes.
Private: Refer to address and number below.
NHS: St Philip's Hospital, Sheffield Street,
London WC2A 2EX. Tel: 071 242 9831.

*Academic: Professor of Nephrology, University College and
Middlesex Medical School. Major degrees: MD, FRCP. First
qualified in London in 1971.*

OGG, Dr C. Stuart.

Especially in relation to kidney stones.
PRIVATE: Emblem House, London Bridge Hospital,
27 Tooley Street, London SE1 2PR.
Tel: 071 403 1221. Fax: 071 407 3162.
NHS: Director, Dialysis and Transplant Unit, Guy's Hospital,
St Thomas Street, London SE1 9RT
Tel: 071 407 7600. Fax: 071 922 8079.

MAJOR DEGREES: MD, FRCP. First qualified (with distinction)
in 1961. Specialist training at Guy's and St Philip's Hospitals.

PARSONS, Dr Victor R. D.

Especially in relation to diabetes and bone disease.
PRIVATE: Refer to address and number below.
NHS: Physician in Charge, Renal Dialysis Unit,
Dulwich Hospital, East Dulwich Grove, London SE22 8PT.
Tel: 071 693 3377.

ACADEMIC: Dean of Postgraduate Studies, King's College
Hospital. MAJOR DEGREE: FRCP. First qualified in Oxford in
1953. Specialist training at King's College Hospital.
USA: Lately Clinical Research Fellow, Harvard Medical
School and Massachusetts General Hospital, Boston.

PHILLIPS, Dr Malcolm E.

PRIVATE: Refer to address and number below.
NHS: Consultant Physician, Charing Cross Hospital,
Fulham Palace Road, London W6 8RF. Tel: 081 846 1747.

MAJOR DEGREES: MD, FRCP. First qualified in London in
1964. Specialist training at Charing Cross Hospital and the
University of Naples.

RAINE, Professor Anthony E. G.

Especially in relation to hypertension.
PRIVATE: Refer to address and number below.
NHS AND ACADEMIC: Professor of Nephrology,
St Bartholomew's Hospital, West Smithfield,
London EC1A 7BE Tel: 071 601 8888. Fax: 071 601 7899.

DISTINCTION: *Councillor, British Hypertension Society.* MAJOR
DEGREES: *DPhil, FRCP. First qualified in New Zealand in
1973. Specialist training at Oxford.*

REES, Professor Andrew J.

Especially in relation to auto-allergies.
PRIVATE: Refer to address and number below.
NHS AND ACADEMIC: Professor of Nephrology,
Royal Postgraduate Medical School, Hammersmith Hospital,
Du Cane Road, London W12 0HS.
Tel 081 743 2030. Fax: 081 740 3169.

DISTINCTION: *Lately Goulstonian Lecturer, Royal College of
Physicians.* MAJOR DEGREE: *FRCP. First qualified in Liverpool
in 1969. Specialist training at the Royal Postgraduate Medical
School.*

TAUBE, Dr H. David.

Especially management of transplants.
PRIVATE: Emblem House, London Bridge Hospital,
27 Tooley Street, London SE1 2PR.
Tel: 071 403 1221. Fax: 071 407 3162
NHS: Consultant Nephrologist, Renal and Dialysis Unit,
Dulwich Hospital, London SE22 8PT. Tel: 081 693 3377.

MAJOR DEGREE: *FRCP. First qualified in Oxford in 1973.
Specialist training at the John Radcliffe Infirmary, Oxford,
and Dulwich Hospital.*

WING, Dr Anthony J.

PRIVATE: Refer to address and number below.
NHS: Consultant Physician, St Thomas's Hospital,
Lambeth Palace Road, London SE1 7EH.
Tel: 071 928 9292. Fax: 071 922 8079.

DISTINCTION: *Chairman, European Dialysis and Transplant Association. Major degrees: DM, FRCP. First qualified in Oxford in 1958. Specialist training at Charing Cross Hospital.*

NEUROLOGISTS

DICK, Dr Jeremy P. R.

PRIVATE: Refer to address and number below.
NHS: Consultant Neurologist, The Royal London Hospital,
Whitechapel Road, London E1 1BB.
Tel: 071 377 7000. Fax: 071 377 7396 or 7122.

MAJOR DEGREE: FRCP. First qualified in Cambridge in 1977.
Specialist training at Charing Cross Hospital.

GAWLER, Dr Jeffrey.

PRIVATE: 109 Harley Street, London W1N 1DG.
Tel: 071 935 7505.
NHS: Consultant Neurologist, St Bartholomew's Hospital,
West Smithfield, London EC1A 7BE.
Tel: 071 601 8888. Fax: 071 601 7899.

MAJOR DEGREE: FRCP. First qualified (with honours) in
London in 1968. Specialist training at the National Hospital
for Nervous Diseases.

GIBBARD, Dr Frederick B.

Especially Refsum's Disease.
PRIVATE: Refer to address and number below.
NHS: Consultant Neurologist, Chelsea and Westminster
Hospital, 369 Fulham Road, London SW10 9NH.
Tel: 081 746 8000. Fax: 081 746 8111.

MAJOR DEGREES: MD, FRCP. First qualified in Cambridge in
1957. Specialist training at the Royal London and National
Hospitals.

GUILOFF, Dr Roberto J.

PRIVATE: Refer to address and number below.
NHS: Consultant Neurologist, Chelsea and Westminster
Hospital, 369 Fulham Road, London SW10 9NH.
Tel: 081 746 8000. Fax: 081 746 8111.

*MAJOR DEGREES: MD, FRCP. First qualified in Santiago,
Chile, in 1967. Specialist training at the National Hospital.*

HARDING, Dr Anita E.

Hereditary ataxias and spinal neurology.
PRIVATE: Refer to address and number below.
NHS AND ACADEMIC: Consultant and Reader in Neurology,
National Hospital, Queen Square, London WC1N 3BG.
Tel: 071 837 3611. Fax: 071 829 8720.

*MAJOR DEGREES: MD, FRCP. First qualified in London in
1975. Specialist training at the Medical Research Council, the
Royal Postgraduate Medical School and the National
Hospital.*

HARVEY, Dr Peter K. P.

Especially epilepsy.
PRIVATE: 134 Harley Street, London W1N 1AH.
Tel: 071 486 8005. Fax: 071 224 3905.
NHS: Consultant Neurologist, Royal Free Hospital,
Pond Street, London NW3 2QG.
Tel: 071 794 0500. Fax: 071 435 5342.

*MAJOR DEGREE: FRCP. First qualified in Cambridge in 1966.
Specialist training at the National Hospital for Nervous
Diseases, London.*

HOPKINS, Dr Anthony P.

Especially seizures.
PRIVATE: 149 Harley Street, London W1N 2DE.
Tel: 071 935 4444. Fax: 071 486 3782.
NHS: Physician in Charge, Department of Neurology,
St Bartholomew's Hospital, West Smithfield,
London EC1A 7BE. Tel: 071 601 8888. Fax: 071 601 7899.

DISTINCTION: Director, Research Unit, Royal College of Physicians. MAJOR DEGREES: MD, FRCP. First qualified in London in 1960. Specialist training at the National Hospital; the Salpetrière Hospital, Paris; and the Mayo Clinic, USA. USA: Member, American Academy Neurologists.

KENNARD, Professor Christopher.

Including neorological ophthalmology.
PRIVATE: Refer to address and number below.
NHS AND ACADEMIC: Professor of Neurology,
Chelsea and Westminster Hospital, 369 Fulham Road,
London SW10 9NH.
Tel: 081 746 8000. Fax: 081 746 8111.

MAJOR DEGREES: Phd, FRCP. First qualified in 1970. Specialist training at the Royal London Hospital. USA: Research Neurologist, University of California Medical Center, San Francisco.

KOCHEN, Dr Roman S.

Especially diagnosis of complex neurological conditions.
PRIVATE: Refer to address and number below.
NHS: Consultant Physician, National Hospital, Queen Square,
London WC1N 3BG.
Tel: 071 837 3611. Fax: 071 829 8720.

DISTINCTIONS: Consultant Neurologist to the Royal Air Force and British Airways. First qualified (with honours) in Leeds in 1956. Specialist training at the National Hospital.

LEGG, Dr Nigel J.

Especially migraine and viral diseases of the nervous system.
PRIVATE: 152 Harley Street, London W1N 1HH.
Tel: 071 935 8868.
NHS: Consultant Neurologist, Hammersmith Hospital,
150 Du Cane Road, London W12 0HS.
Tel: 081 749 9646. Fax: 081 740 3169.

ACADEMIC: Senior Lecturer in Neurology, Royal Postgraduate Medical School. MAJOR DEGREE: FRCP. First qualified (with honours) in London in 1959. Specialist training at the National Hospital for Nervous Diseases.

LUXON, Dr Linda M.

Especially vertigo, neurological disorders of the ear and the eye.
PRIVATE: 47 Weymouth Street, London W1N 3LD.
Tel: 071 486 5787.
NHS: Consultant Physician in Neuro-Otology,
National Hospital, Queen Square, London WC1N 3BG.
Tel: 071 837 3611. Fax: 071 829 8720.

DISTINCTION: Secretary, British Association of Audiological Physicians.MAJOR DEGREE: FRCP. First qualified in London in 1972. Specialist training at the National Hospital for Nervous Diseases.

MARSDEN, Professor C. David.

Movement disorders, including Parkinson's disease.
PRIVATE: Refer to address and number below.
NHS: Consultant Neurologist, National Hospital,
Queen Square, London WC1N 3BG.
Tel: 071 837 3611. Fax: 071 829 8720.

ACADEMIC: *Professor of Neurology, Institute of Neurology.*
MAJOR DEGREES: DSC, FRCP, FRCPsych. First qualified in
London in 1963. Specialist training at King's College Hospital
and the Maudsley Hospital.

MEADOWS, Dr John C.

PRIVATE: 143 Harley Street, London W1N 1DJ.
Tel: 071 935 1802.
NHS: Resigned.

ACADEMIC: *Senior Lecturer, St George's Hospital. MAJOR*
DEGREES: MD, FRCP. First graduated (with double-first class
honours) in Cambridge in 1964. Specialist training at the
National Hospital for Nervous Diseases.

MORGAN-HUGHES, Dr John A.

Especially muscular disorders.
PRIVATE: Refer to address and number below.
NHS: Consultant Physician, National Hospital,
Queen Square, London WC1N 3BG.
Tel: 071 837 3611. Fax: 071 829 8720.

MAJOR DEGREES: MD, FRCP. First qualified in Cambridge in
1957. USA: Lately Fellow, National Institute of Health,
Bethesda, Maryland.

PARKES, Professor J. David.

Myasthenia, Parkinson's disease and narcolepsy.
PRIVATE: See address and number below.
NHS AND ACADEMIC: Professor of Neurology,
King's College Hospital, Denmark Hill, London SE5 9RS.
Tel: 071 274 6222. Fax: 071 326 3589.

MAJOR DEGREES: MD, FRCP. First qualified in Cambridge in 1964. Specialist training at the Maudsley and National Hospitals.

REYNOLDS, Dr Edward H.

Especially epilepsy.
PRIVATE: Refer to address and number below.
NHS: Consultant Neurologist, Maudsley Hospital,
Denmark Hill, London SE5 8AZ.
Tel: 071 703 6333. Fax: 071 919 2171.

ACADEMIC: Senior Lecturer, Department of Neurology, Institute of Psychiatry. Distinction: Secretary, League Against Epilepsy. MAJOR DEGREES: MD, FRCP. First qualified in Cardiff in 1959. Specialist training at the National Hospital and the Medical Research Council, Neuropsychiatric Research Unit. USA: Lately Assistant Professor, Yale University Medical School.

ROSSOR, Dr Martin N.

Alzheimer's disease.
PRIVATE: Refer to address and number below.
NHS: Consultant Neurologist, St Mary's Hospital,
Praed Street, London W2 1NY.
Tel: 071 262 1280 or 725 6666. Fax: 071 725 6200.

MAJOR DEGREES: MD, FRCP. First qualified in Cambridge in

1975. Specialist training at Cambridge, King's College Hospital and the National Hospital.

THOMAS, Dr David J.

Especially strokes.
PRIVATE: Refer to number below.
Tel: 071 725 1389. Fax: 0753 662147.
NHS: Consultant Neurologist, St Mary's Hospital,
Praed Street, London W2 1NY.
Tel: 071 262 1280 or 725 6666. Fax: 071 725 6200.

DISTINCTION: Chairman, British Stroke Foundation. MAJOR DEGREES: MD, FRCP. First qualified in Cambridge in 1970. Specialist training at Queen Elizabeth Hospital, Birmingham, St Thomas's and the National Hospitals.

ZILKHA, Dr Kevin J.

Especially dietary and hormonal factors in migraine and multiple sclerosis.
PRIVATE: Refer to address and number below.
NHS: Senior Consultant Neurologist, King's College Hospital,
Denmark Hill, London SE5 9RS.
Tel: 071 274 6222. Fax: 071 326 3589.

DISTINCTIONS: Physician, National Hospital; Honorary Consultant to the Maudsley, the Army and the Royal Hospital, Chelsea. MAJOR DEGREES: MD, FRCP. First qualified in London in 1953. Specialist training at Guy's and the National Hospitals.

NEUROSURGEONS

AFSHAR, Mr Farhad.

PRIVATE: 109 Harley Street, London W1N 1DG.
Tel: 071 935 7504.
NHS: Consultant Neurosurgeon, St Bartholomew's Hospital,
West Smithfield, London EC1A 7BE.
Tel: 071 601 8888. Fax: 071 601 7899.

*MAJOR DEGREES: MD, FRCS. First qualified in London in
1967. Specialist training at St Bartholomew's and the Royal
London hospitals. USA: Lately Fellow in Neurosurgery, Ohio
State University, Columbus; Consultant Neurosurgeon,
Hartford, Connecticut.*

CROCKARD, Mr Hugh A.

Especially the spine.
PRIVATE: Refer to address and number below.
NHS: Consultant Neurosurgeon, National Hospital,
Queen Square, London WC1N 3BG.
Tel: 071 636 4191. Fax: 071 829 8720.

*DISTINCTIONS: Co-founder and secretary, British Cervical
Spine Society; Chairman, Neurosurgical Implants Committee,
International Standards Organisation; lately, Hunterian
Professor, Royal College of Surgeons. MAJOR DEGREE: FRCS.
First qualified in Belfast in 1966. Specialist training at the
National Hospital, Belfast.*

GRANT, Mr David N.

Including children.
PRIVATE: Refer to address and number below.
NHS: Consultant Neurosurgeon, National Hospital,
Queen Square, London WC1N 3BG.
Tel: 071 837 3611. Fax: 071 829 8720

and the Hospital for Sick Children, 34 Great Ormond Street, London WC1N 3JH. Tel: 071 405 9200. Fax: 071 829 8643.

DISTINCTION: *Honorary Consultant Neurosurgeon to the Royal Air Force.* MAJOR DEGREE: *FRCS. First qualified in St Andrews in 1958. Specialist training in St Andrews; at the Alfred Hospital, Melbourne, Australia and the National Hospital.*

HAYWARD, Mr Richard D.

Especially head injuries, including children's.
PRIVATE: Refer to address and number below.
NHS: National Hospital, Queen Square, London WC1N 3BG. Tel: 071 837 3611. Fax: 071 829 8720.

MAJOR DEGREE: *FRCS. First qualified in London in 1966. Specialist training at St Mary's and the National Hospital.*

ILLINGWORTH, Mr Robert D.

PRIVATE: 152 Harley Street, London W1N 1HH.
Tel: 071 935 0444.
NHS: Consulting Neurosurgeon, Charing Cross Hospital, Fulham Palace Road, London W6 8RF.
Tel: 081 846 1234. Fax: 081 846 1111.

MAJOR DEGREE: *FRCS. First qualified in London in 1958. Specialist training at the Middlesex and National Hospitals.*

POWELL, Mr Michael P.

PRIVATE: Refer to address and number below.
NHS: Consultant Neurosurgeon, Middlesex Hospital,
Mortimer Street, London W1N 8AA.
Tel: 071 636 8333. Fax: 071 323 0397.
MAJOR DEGREE: FRCS. First qualified in London in 1975.
Specialist training at the National Hospital.

THOMAS, Mr David G. T.

Especially head injuries and brain tumours.
PRIVATE: Refer to address and number below.
NHS: Consultant Neurosurgeon, National Hospital,
Queen Square, London WC1N 3BG.
Tel: 071 837 3611. Fax: 071 829 8720.

ACADEMIC: Senior Lecturer, Institute of Neurology.
Distinctions: Consultant Neurosurgeon, Medical Research
Council. Prizes and fellowships awarded by the Royal College
of Surgeons, Wellcome Foundation etc. MAJOR DEGREES:
FRCP, FRCS. First qualified in Cambridge in 1966. Specialist
training at the Institute of Neurological Science, Glasgow, and
St Mary's Hospital.

OBSTETRICIANS AND GYNAECOLOGISTS

ARMSTRONG, Mr N. Paul.

Pregnancy.
PRIVATE: Portland Hospital, 209 Great Portland Street,
London W1N 6AH. Tel: 071 580 4400. Fax: 071 631 1170.
NHS: Consultant Obstetrician and Gynaecologist,
Central Middlesex Hospital, Acton Lane, Park Royal,
London NW10 7NS. Tel: 081 965 5733.

ACADEMIC: *Senior Lecturer in Obstetrics and Gynaecology,
St Mary's.* MAJOR DEGREES: *MD, FRCOG. First qualified in
Manchester in 1976. Specialist training at University College
and the Royal London Hospitals.*

BEARD, Professor Richard W.

Including diabetic pregnancy and pelvic pain.
PRIVATE: Refer to address and number below.
NHS AND ACADEMIC: Professor of Obstetrics and
Gynaecology, St Mary's Hospital, Praed Street,
London W2 1NY.
Tel: 071 725 1461. Fax: 071 725 6200.

DISTINCTIONS: *Chairman, Royal College of Obstetrics and
Gynaecology; Adviser on Obstetrics and Gynaecology to the
Department of Health; Civilian Consultant to the Royal Air
Force.* MAJOR DEGREES: *MD, FRCOG. First qualified in
London in 1956. Specialist training at King's and Queen
Charlotte's Hospitals.*

CAMPBELL, Professor Stuart.

Prenatal diagnosis.
PRIVATE: Refer to address and number below.
NHS AND ACADEMIC: Professor of Obstetrics and
Gynaecology, King's College Hospital, Denmark Hill,

London SE5 9RS. Tel: 071 274 6222. Fax: 071 326 3589.

MAJOR DEGREE: FRCOG. First qualified in Glasgow in 1961. Specialist training at Queen Charlotte's Hospital, London. USA: Fellow, American Institute of Ultrasound.

CARDOSO, Ms Linda

Especially female incontinence.
PRIVATE: 8 Devonshire Place, London W1N 1PB.
Tel: 071 935 2357.
NHS: Consultant Obstetrician and Gynaecologist,
King's College Hospital, Denmark Hill, London SE5 9RS.
Tel: 071 274 6222. Fax: 071 326 3589.

MAJOR DEGREES: MD, FRCOG. First qualified in 1974. Specialist training at St George's Hospital.

CHAMBERLAIN, Professor Geoffrey V.

Care of the foetus.
PRIVATE: Refer to address and number below.
NHS AND ACADEMIC: Professor of Obstetrics and Gynaecology, St George's Hospital, Blackshaw Road, London SW17 0QT.

DISTINCTIONS: Editor, Contemporary Review of Obstetrics and Gynaecology; Examiner to many universities in Britain and abroad; Visiting Professor, Hong Kong, Australia etc. MAJOR DEGREES: MD, FRCOG. First qualified in London in 1954. Specialist training at Queen Charlotte's Hospital, London. USA: Beckman Professor, Foundation Professor, American Association of Obstetrics and Gynaecology.

Brought Robs into the world!

COLTART, Mr Timothy M.

PRIVATE: 92 Harley Street, London W1N 1AF.
Tel: 071 935 6836.
NHS: Consultant Obstetrician and Gynaecologist,
Guy's Hospital, St Thomas Street, London SE1 9RT.
Tel: 071 928 9292. Fax: 071 922 8079.

MAJOR DEGREES: *PhD, FRCS, FRCOG. First qualified in Cambridge in 1963. Specialist training at Queen Charlotte's Hospital.*

FRASER, Mr Alasdair C.

PRIVATE: 100 Harley Street, London W1N 1AF.
Tel: 071 935 9367.
NHS: Consultant Obstetrician and Gynaecologist,
St Mary's Hospital, Praed Street, London W2 1NY.
Tel: 071 262 1280. Fax: 071 725 6200.

DISTINCTION: *Examiner, Royal College of Obstetricians and Gynaecologists.* MAJOR DEGREE: *FRCOG. First qualified in London in 1953. Specialist training at St Mary's Hospital.*

GILLARD, Mr Malcolm G.

Pregnancy.
PRIVATE: 31 Weymouth Street, London W1N 3FJ.
Tel: 071 580 4499.
NHS: None

DISTINCTIONS: *Lately Dean, Institute of Obstetrics and Gynaecology; Hallet Prize, Royal College of Surgeons.* MAJOR DEGREES: *FRCS, FRCOG. First qualified (with honours) in London in 1972. Specialist training at Queen Charlotte's Hospital.*

KENNEY, Mr Anthony.

PRIVATE: 17 Wimpole Street, London W1M 7AD.
Tel: 081 942 0440.
NHS: Consultant Obstetrician and Gynaecologist,
St Thomas's Hospital, Lambeth Palace Road,
London SE1 7EH. Tel: 071 928 9292.

DISTINCTION *Examiner, Royal College of Obstetrics and Gynaecology. MAJOR DEGREES: FRCS, FRCOG. First qualified in Cambridge in 1966. Specialist training at the London and Westminster Hospitals.*

LLOYD, Mrs Ursula.

PRIVATE: Portland Hospital, 209 Great Portland Street,
London W1N 6AH. Tel: 071 935 3732. Fax: 071 631 1170.
NHS: Consultant Obstetrician and Gynaecologist,
St George's Hospital, Blackshaw Road, London SW17 0QT.
Tel: 081 672 1255.

MAJOR DEGREE: *FRCOG. First qualified in London in 1967. Specialist training at Queen Charlotte's Hospital and the Chelsea Hospital for Women.*

LOEFFLER, Mr Frank E.

Especially detection of foetal abnormalities during pregnancy.
PRIVATE: 86 Harley Street, London W1N 1AE.
Tel: 071 486 2966.
NHS: Consultant Obstetrician and Gynaecologist,
St Mary's Hospital, Praed Street, London W2 1NY.
Tel: 071 262 1280 or 725 6666. Fax: 071 725 6200.

DISTINCTION: *Lately Editor,* British Journal of Obstetrics and

Gynaecology. *MAJOR DEGREES: FRCS, FRCOG. First qualified in Cambridge in 1956. Specialist training at Queen Charlotte's Hospital.*

McMillan, Mr Lindsay.

Minimally invasive surgery.
PRIVATE: 17 Wimpole Street, London W1M 7AD.
Tel: 071 631 0914.
NHS: Consultant Gynaecologist, Whipp's Cross Hospital, Whipp's Cross Road, Leytonstone, London E11 1NR.
Tel: 081 539 5522.

MAJOR DEGREE: FRCOG. First qualified in London. Specialist training at King's College Hospital.

MAGOS, Mr Adam L.

Minimally invasive surgery.
PRIVATE: Refer to address and number below.
NHS: Consultant, Academic Department of Obstetrics and Gynaecology, Royal Free Hospital, Pond Street, London NW3 2QG. Tel: 071 794 0500. Fax: 071 435 5342.

MAJOR DEGREES: MD, FRCOG. First qualified in London in 1978. Specialist training at the John Radcliffe Infirmary, Oxford, and King's College Hospital.

MALVERN, Mr John

Especially incontinence.
PRIVATE: 84 Harley Street, London W1N 1AE.
Tel: 071 636 2766.
NHS: Consultant Gynaecologist, Chelsea Hospital for Women, Dovehouse Street, London SW3 6LJ. Tel: 071 352 6446.

ACADEMIC: Senior Lecturer, Institute of Obstetrics and Gynaecology. DISTINCTIONS: Councillor and Examiner, Royal College of Obstetrics and Gynaecology. MAJOR DEGREES: FRCS, FRCOG. First qualified in London in 1960. Specialist training at Queen Charlotte's Hospital and the Chelsea Hospital for Women.

MARWOOD, Mr Roger P.

Gynaecology.
PRIVATE: 80 Harley Street, London W1N 1AE.
Tel: 071 637 7577.
NHS: Consultant Obstetrician and Gynaecologist, Chelsea and Westminster Hospital, 369 Fulham Road, SW10 9NH.
Tel: 081 746 8000. Fax: 081 746 8111.

MAJOR DEGREE: FRCOG. First qualified in London in 1969. Specialist training at Guy's and St Mary's Hospitals.

MASON, Mr Peter W.

Especially cancer.
PRIVATE: 106 Harley Street, London W1N 1AF.
Tel: 071 935 7952.
NHS: Consultant Obstetrician and Gynaecologist,
St Mary's Hospital, Praed Street, London W2 1NY.
Tel: 071 262 1280 or 725 6666. Fax: 071 725 6200.

MAJOR DEGREES: FRCS, FRCOG. First qualified in Bristol in 1972. Specialist training at St Mary's Hospital.

NICOLAEDES, Mr Kyprianos H.

Prenatal diagnosis and treatment of the foetus.
PRIVATE: Refer to address and number below.

NHS: Consultant, Harris Birthright Research Centre for Foetal Medicine, King's College Hospital Medical School, Denmark Hill, London SE5 9RS.
Tel: 071 274 6222. Fax: 071 326 3589.

MAJOR DEGREE: FRCOG. First qualified in London in 1978. Specialist training at King's College Hospital.

ORAM, Mr David H.

Especially gynaecological cancer.
PRIVATE: 121 Harley Street, London W1N 1DM.
Tel: 071 935 7111.
NHS: Consultant Obstetrician and Gynaecologist, Royal London Hospital, Whitechapel, London E1 1BB.
Tel: 071 377 7000. Fax: 071 377 7396 or 7122.

MAJOR DEGREE: FRCOG. First qualified in London in 1971. Specialist training in Durban, South Africa, and at the University of Georgetown, Washington, DC.

PAWSON, Mr. Michael E.

Especially holistic gynaecology.
PRIVATE: 55 Wimpole Street, London W1. Tel: 071 935 1964.
NHS AND ACADEMIC: Senior Lecturer and Consultant in Gynaecology, Chelsea and Westminster Hospital, 369 Fulham Road, London SW10 9NH. Tel: 081 746 8000. Fax: 081 746 8111.

DISTINCTIONS: Examiner, University of London and Royal College of Obstetrics and Gynaecology. MAJOR DEGREE: FRCOG. First qualified in London, in 1962. Specialist training at Queen Charlotte's Hospital.

SAVVAS, Mr Michael.

Especially PMT and menopause.
PRIVATE: Refer to address and number below.
NHS: Consultant Obstetrician and Gynaecologist,
Lewisham Hospital, High Street, Lewisham,
London SW13 6LH. Tel: 081 690 4311.

MAJOR DEGREE: *FRCOG. First qualified in London in 1980.*
Specialist training at King's College Hospital.

SETCHELL, Mr Marcus E.

Including fertility.
PRIVATE: 137 Harley Street, London W1N 1DJ.
Tel: 071 935 6122.
and Director, Fertility Clinic, Portland Hospital,
209 Great Portland Street, London W1N 6AH.
Tel: 071 580 4400. Fax: 071 631 1170.
NHS: Senior Consultant Gynaecologist and Obstetrician,
St Bartholomew's and Homerton Hospitals, Homerton Row,
London E9 6SR. Tel: 071 985 5555.
and Director, In-Vitro Fertilisation Clinic,
St Bartholomew's Hospital, West Smithfield,
London EC1A 7BE. Tel: 071 601 8888. Fax: 071 601 7899.

DISTINCTIONS: *Gynaecologist to HM the Queen; Examiner to*
the universities of London and Cambridge and the Royal
College of Obstetricians and Gynaecologists. MAJOR DEGREES:
FRCS, FRCOG. First qualified in Cambridge in 1968.

SHEPHERD, Mr John.

Gynaecological cancer.
PRIVATE: 40 Harley Street, London W1N 1DJ.
Tel: 071 935 7054.
NHS: Consultant Gynaecological Surgeon and Oncologist,

St Bartholomew's Hospital, West Smithfield,
London EC1A 7BE.
Tel: 071 601 8888. Fax: 071 601 7899.

*DISTINCTION: Lately Royal College of Obstetricians and
Gynaecologists Gold Medallist. MAJOR DEGREES: FRCS,
FACOG, FRCOG. First qualified in London in 1971.
Specialist training at Queen Charlotte's Hospital and the
Chelsea Hospital for Women, London. USA: Visiting
Professor, universities of Virginia and South Florida.*

SILVERSTONE, Mr Anthony C.

Gynaecological cancer.
PRIVATE: Portland Hospital, 209 Great Portland Street,
London W1N 6AH. Tel: 071 580 4400. Fax: 071 631 1170.
NHS: Consultant Obstetrician and Gynaecologist,
Middlesex Hospital, Mortimer Street, London W1N 8AA.
Tel: 071 636 8333. Fax: 071 323 0397.

*MAJOR DEGREES: FRCS, FRCOG. First qualified in
Birmingham in 1969. Specialist training at the John Radcliffe
Infirmary, Oxford, and Queen Charlotte's Hospital.*

SINGER, Professor Albert.

Especially non-surgical treatment of gynaecological problems.
PRIVATE: 148 Harley Street, London W1N 1DJ.
Tel: 071 935 1900. Fax: 081 458 0168.
NHS AND ACADEMIC: Professor of Gynaecology,
The Wittington Hospital, London N19 5NF.
Tel: 071 272 9540.

*ACADEMIC: Clinical Senior Lecturer, University College.
DISTINCTION: Hon. Consultant, Hammersmith. MAJOR
DEGREES: PhD, DPhil, FRCOG. First qualified in Sydney,
Australia, in 1962. Specialist training at Oxford and Sheffield.*

STANTON, Mr Stuart L. R.

Female incontinence.
PRIVATE: Flat 10, 43 Wimpole Street, London WIM 7AF.
Tel: 071 935 5117. Fax: 071 486 6792.
NHS: Consultant Gynaecologist, St George's Hospital,
Blackshaw Road, London SW17 0QT.
Tel: 071 672 1255.

ACADEMIC: *Senior Lecturer, St George's Hospital Medical
School.* DISTINCTION: *Examiner, Royal College of
Obstetricians and Gynaecologists.* MAJOR DEGREE: *FRCOG.
First qualified in London in 1961. Specialist training at the
Middlesex Hospital.*

STEER, Professor Philip J.

Foetal monitoring.
PRIVATE: Refer to address and number below.
NHS AND ACADEMIC: Professor of Obstetrics,
Charing Cross Hospital, Fulham Palace Road,
London W6 8RF. Tel: 081 846 1234.

DISTINCTION: *Councillor, British Association of Perinatal
Medicine.* MAJOR DEGREES: *MD, FRCOG. First qualified in
London in 1971. Specialist training at Queen Charlotte's
Hospital.*

STUDD, Mr John W. W.

Especially premenstrual tension, menopause and infertility.
PRIVATE: 120 Harley Street, London W1N 1AG.
Tel: 071 486 0497.
and Director, Infertility and Endocrine Centre, Lister Hospital,
Chelsea Bridge Road, London SW1W 8RH.
Tel: 071 730 5433. Fax: 071 823 6108.
NHS: Consultant Obstetrician and Gynaecologist,

Chelsea and Westminster Hospital, 369 Fulham Road,
London SW10 9NH. Tel: 081 746 8000. Fax: 081 746 8111.

*DISTINCTIONS: President, International Society of
Reproductive Medicine; Chairman, National Osteoporosis
Society; Examiner to the RCOG and the universities of
London, Birmingham, Cambridge and Nottingham. MAJOR
DEGREES: MD, FRCOG. First qualified in Birmingham in
1962. Specialist training at the university hospitals of
Birmingham and Nottingham. USA: Visiting Professor, Yale
and Duke Universities.*

THOM, Ms Margaret H.

Including pregnancy.
PRIVATE: 97 Harley Street, London W1 1DE.
Tel: 071 496 9272.
NHS: Consultant Obstetrician and Gynaecologist,
Guy's Hospital, St Thomas Street, London SE1 9RT.
Tel: 071 955 5000. Fax: 071 922 8079.

*First qualified in London in 1973. Specialist training at Queen
Charlotte's Hospital, the Chelsea Hospital for Women and
King's College Hospital*

VERSI, Mr Eboo.

Especially female incontinence.
NHS: Consultant in Obstetrics and Gynaecology at
St Thomas's Hospital, Lambeth Palace Road,
London SE1 7EH.
Tel: 071 928 9292.

*MAJOR DEGREES: DPhil, FRCOG. First qualified in Cambridge
in 1980. Specialist training at King's College and Royal
London Hospitals.*

N, **Professor Robert M. L.**

ertility.

PRIVATE: Refer to address and number below.
NHS: Consultant Gynaecologist, Hammersmith Hospital,
Du Cane Road, London W12 0HS.
Tel: 081 743 2030. Fax: 081 740 3169.

ACADEMIC: *Professor of Fertility Studies, Royal Postgraduate Medical School.* MAJOR DEGREES: *MD, FRCOG. Specialist training at the Royal Postgraduate Medical School.*

OPHTHALMOLOGISTS

ARNOTT, Mr Eric L.

Especially cataract surgery and correction of short sight by laser. Biggest private practice in London: has team of ophthalmologists at the Cromwell Hospital.
PRIVATE: Arnott Ophthalmic Clinic, Cromwell Hospital, Cromwell Road, London SW5 0TU.
Tel: 071 835 1035. Fax: 071 835 1456.
NHS: Consultant Ophthalmic Surgeon,
Charing Cross Hospital, Fulham Palace Road,
London W6 8RF. Tel: 081 748 2040. Fax: 081 846 1111.

DISTINCTION: Director, International Phacoemulsificat and Cataract Methodology Society. MAJOR DEGREES: FRCS, FCOphth. First qualified in Dublin in 1954. Specialist training at Moorfields and University College Hospitals.

BLACH, Mr Rudolf K.

Especially the retina.
PRIVATE: Lister House, 11/12 Wimpole Street,
London W1M 7AB. Tel: 071 636 3407.
NHS: Consultant Surgeon, Moorfields Eye Hospital,
City Road, London EC1V 2PD.
Tel: 071 253 3411. Fax: 071 253 4696.

ACADEMIC: Lately Dean, Institute of Ophthalmology. DISTINCTIONS: Consultant Ophthalmologist, Royal Postgraduate Medical School; Senior Ophthalmology Consultant, St Dunstan's. MAJOR DEGREES: MD, FRCS, FCOphth. First qualified in Cambridge in 1956. Specialist training at Moorfields Eye Hospital.

CHIGNELL, Mr Anthony H.

Especially retinal detachment.
PRIVATE: 44 Wimpole Street, London W1M 7DG.
Tel: 071 935 7022.
NHS: Consultant Ophthalmologist, St Thomas's Hospital,
Lambeth Palace Road, London SE1 7EH.
Tel: 071 928 9292. Fax: 071 922 8079.

DISTINCTION: Consultant Ophthalmologist to the Army.
MAJOR DEGREES: FRCS, FCOphth. First qualified in London
in 1962. Specialist training at Moorfields and St Thomas's
Hospitals.

COOLING, Mr Robert J.

Especially injuries to the eye.
PRIVATE: 18 Wimpole Street, London W1M 7AD.
Tel: 071 935 4536. Fax: 071 637 2489.
NHS: Consultant Surgeon, Moorfields Eye Hospital,
City Road, London EC1V 2PD.
Tel: 071 253 3411. Fax: 071 253 4696.

DISTINCTION: Honorary Consultant to the Royal Navy. MAJOR
DEGREES: FRCS, FCOphth. First qualified (with honours) in
Liverpool in 1970. Specialist training at Moorfields.

DANIEL, Mr Reginald.

General eye surgery.
PRIVATE: Emblem House, London Bridge Hospital,
27 Tooley Street, SE1 2PR.
Tel: 071 403 4884. Fax: 071 407 3162.
NHS: Consultant Ophthalmologist, Guy's Hospital,
St Thomas Street, London SE1 9RT. Tel: 071 955 5000.

MAJOR DEGREES: FRCS, FCOphth. First qualified in London

in 1964. Specialist training at Professorial Surgical Unit,
Westminster and Moorfields Eye Hospitals.

DART, Mr John K. G.

Especially the cornea.
PRIVATE: 8 Upper Wimpole Street, London W1M 7TD.
Tel: 071 486 2257.
NHS: Consultant Ophthalmologist, Moorfields Eye Hospital,
City Road, London EC1V 2PD.
Tel: 071 253 3411. Fax: 071 253 4696.

ACADEMIC: *Clinical Lecturer, Institute of Ophthalmology.*
MAJOR DEGREES: *FRCS (Ophth) FCOphth. First qualified*
in Oxford in 1976. Specialist training at Moorfields.

DAVIES, Mr E. W. Geoffrey.

Especially eye problems of diabetics, and retinal detachment.
PRIVATE: 127 Harley Street, London W1N 1DJ.
Tel: 071 580 1631.
NHS: Consultant Ophthalmic Surgeon,
King's College Hospital, Denmark Hill, London SE5 9RS.
Tel: 071 274 6222. Fax: 071 326 3428.

MAJOR DEGREES: *FRCS, FCOphth. First qualified in*
Cambridge in 1955. Specialist training at St Mary's and
Moorfields Eye Hospitals.

FALCON, Mr Michael G.

Especially the cornea.
PRIVATE: 25 Wimpole Street, London W1M 7AD.
Tel: 071 580 7199.

NHS: Consultant Surgeon in Ophthalmology,

St Thomas's Hospital, Lambeth Palace Road,
London SE1 7EH. Tel: 071 928 9292. Fax: 071 922 8079.

MAJOR DEGREES: *FRCP, FRCS, FCOphth. First qualified in
Cambridge in 1967. Specialist training at Moorfields Eye
Hospital.*

FELLS. Mr Peter.

*Orthoptics – training in overcoming squints
and double vision.*
PRIVATE: Refer to address and number below.
NHS: Director Orthoptic Unit, Moorfields Eye Hospital,
City Road, London EC1V 2PD.
Tel: 071 253 3411. Fax: 071 253 4696.

DISTINCTION: *Member, Court of Examiners, Royal College of
Surgeons.* MAJOR DEGREES: *FRCS, FCOphth. First qualified in
Cambridge in 1959. Specialist training at the Royal
Postgraduate Medical School and Moorfields Eye Hospitals.*
USA: *Lately Fellow in Ophthalmology, Columbia
Presbyterian Hospital, New York.*

FFYTCHE, Mr Timothy J.

*Especially the retina and tropical eye diseases. Reputation for
aloofness.*
PRIVATE: 149 Harley Street, London W1N 2DE.
Tel: 071 935 4444. Fax: 071 486 3782.
NHS: Consultant Ophthalmic Surgeon, St Thomas's Hospital,
Lambeth Palace Road, London SE1 7EH.
Tel: 071 928 9292. Fax: 071 922 8079.

DISTINCTION: *Surgeon Oculist to the Royal Household.* MAJOR
DEGREES: *FRCS, FCOphth. First qualified in London in 1961.
Specialist training at the Middlesex and Moorfields Hospitals.*

GREGOR, Mr Zdenek.

Especially retinal surgery.
PRIVATE: Refer to address and number below.
NHS: Consultant Ophthalmic Surgeon,
Moorfields Eye Hospital, City Road, London EC1V 2PD.
Tel: 071 253 3411. Fax: 071 253 4696.

ACADEMIC: Senior Lecturer, Institute of Ophthalmology.
MAJOR DEGREES: FRCS, FCOphth. First qualified in London
in 1971. Specialist training at Moorfields. USA: Lately
Assistant Professor, University of Southern California, Los
Angeles.

HAMILTON, Mr Andrew M.

Especially eye problems of diabetics.
PRIVATE: 149 Harley Street, London W1N 1HG.
Tel: 071 935 4444. Fax: 071 486 3782.
NHS: Consultant Ophthalmologist, Moorfields Eye Hospital,
City Road, London EC1V 2PD.
Tel: 071 253 3411. Fax: 071 253 4696.

MAJOR DEGREES: FRCS, FCOphth. First qualified in London
in 1964. Specialist at the Middlesex and Moorfields Hospitals.

HITCHINGS, Mr Roger A.

Especially glaucoma.
PRIVATE: 36 Devonshire Place, London W1N 1PE.
Tel: 071 486 6987.
NHS: Consultant Ophthalmologist, Moorfields Eye Hospital,
City Road, London EC1V 2PD.
Tel: 071 253 3411. Fax: 071 253 4696.

DISTINCTION: Executive Member, European Glaucoma
Society. MAJOR DEGREES: FRCS, FCOphth. First qualified in

London in 1966. Specialist training at Moorfields.
USA: Lately Clinical Fellow in Ophthalmology,
Wills Eye Hospital, Philadelphia.

HOLMES SELLORS, Mr Patrick J.

Respected medical-legal opinion concerning eyes.
PRIVATE: 149 Harley Street, London W1N 1HJ.
Tel: 071 935 4444. Fax: 071 486 3782.
NHS: Part-time Consultant, Croydon Eye Unit,
Mayday Hospital, Mayday Road, Thornton Heath,
Surrey CR4 7YE. Tel: 081 684 6999.

DISTINCTIONS: *Ophthalmic Surgeon to HM the Queen;*
Councillor, Faculty of Ophthalmology. MAJOR DEGREES:
FRCS, FCOphth. First qualified in Oxford in 1958. Specialist
training at the Middlesex and Moorfields Hospitals.

HUNGERFORD, Mr John L.

Especially cancer of the eye.
PRIVATE: 114 Harley Street, London W1N 1AJ.
Tel: 071 935 1565.
NHS: Consultant, Moorfields Eye Hospital, City Road,
London EC1V 2PD.
Tel: 071 253 3411. Fax: 071 253 4696.

MAJOR DEGREES: *FRCS, FCOphth. First qualified in 1969.*

HUNTER, Mr Paul A.

PRIVATE: 94 Harley Street, London W1N 1AF.
Tel: 071 935 0777.
NHS: Consultant Ophthalmic Surgeon,

King's College Hospital, Denmark Hill, London SE5 9RS.
Tel: 071 274 6222. Fax: 071 326 3589.

*MAJOR DEGREES: FRCS, FCOphth. First qualified in
Cambridge in 1970. Specialist training at the Middlesex and
Moorfields Eye Hospitals.*

JAGGER, Mr Jonathan D.

Especially the retina.
PRIVATE: 2 Harley Street, London W1N 1AA.
Tel: 071 935 3934.
NHS: Consultant Ophthalmologist, Royal Free Hospital,
Pond Street, London NW3 2QG.
Tel: 071 794 0500. Fax: 071 435 5342.

*MAJOR DEGREES: FRCS, FCOphth. First qualified in London
in 1974. Specialist training at Moorfields Eye Hospital.*

KOHNER, Professor Eva M.

Retinal problems of diabetics.
PRIVATE: Refer to address and number below.
NHS: Consultant Physician, Hammersmith Hospital,
150 Du Cane Road, London W12 0HS.
Tel: 081 743 2030. Fax: 081 740 3169.

*ACADEMIC: Professor of Medical Ophthalmology, Royal
Postgraduate Medical School. MAJOR DEGREES: MD, FRCP.
First qualified in London in 1959.*

KERR MUIR, Mr Malcolm G.

Especially laser correction of short sight.
PRIVATE: 9 Upper Wimpole Street, London W1M 7TD.

Tel: 071 935 5038.
NHS: St Thomas's Hospital, Lambeth Palace Road,
London SE1 7EH. Tel: 071 928 9292. Fax: 071 922 8079.

MAJOR DEGREES: FRCS, FCOphth. First qualified in London in 1970. Specialist training in Liverpool and at St Thomas's.

LEAVER, Mr Peter K.

General ophthalmology.
PRIVATE: 114 Harley Street, London W1N 1AG.
Tel: 071 935 1565.
NHS: Consultant Ophthalmologist, Moorfields Eye Hospital,
City Road, London EC1V 2PD.
Tel: 071 253 3411. Fax: 071 253 4696.

MAJOR DEGREES: FRCS, FCOphth. First qualified in London in 1963. Specialist training at the Royal Postgraduate Medical School, St Bartholomew's and Moorfields.

LEE, Mr John P.

Especially squints.
PRIVATE: 62 Wimpole Street, London W1M 7DE.
Tel: 071 935 5801.
NHS: Consultant Ophthalmic Surgeon,
Moorfields Eye Hospital, City Road, London EC1V 2PD.
Tel: 071 253 3411. Fax: 071 253 4696.

ACADEMIC: Clinical Sub-Dean, Institute of Ophthalmology. MAJOR DEGREES: FRCS, FCOphth. First qualified in Oxford in 1971. Specialist training at Moorfields. USA: Fellow of Paediatric and Neuro-Ophthalmic Eye Institute, Miami.

LEVY, Mr Ivor S.

Especially neuro-ophthalmology and laser surgery, including correction of short sight.
PRIVATE: 75 Harley Street, London W1N 1DE.
Tel: 071 486 1138. Fax: 071 224 6214.
NHS: Senior Consultant Ophthalmic Surgeon,
Royal London Hospital, Whitechapel Road, London E1 1BB.
Tel: 071 377 7000. Fax: 071 377 7396 or 7122.

MAJOR DEGREES: FRCP, FRCS, FCOphth. First qualified in London in 1965. Specialist training at Moorfields Eye Hospital. USA: Visiting Professor, Cleveland Clinic.

MARSH, Mr Ronald J.

General ophthalmology.
PRIVATE: 2 Harley Street, London W1N 1AA.
Tel: 071 935 9475.
NHS: Consultant, Western Ophthalmic Hospital,
Marylebone Road, London NW1. Tel: 071 402 4211.

MAJOR DEGREES: FRCS, FCOphth. First qualified (with honours) in London in 1963. Specialist training at Western Ophthalmic and Moorfields Eye Hospitals.

MIGDAL, Mr Clive

Especially glaucoma.
PRIVATE: 3 Park Square West, London NW1 4LJ.
Tel: 071 224 6740.
NHS: Consultant Ophthalmologist,
Western Ophthalmic Hospital, Marylebone Road,
London NW1. Tel: 071 402 4211.

ACADEMIC: Research Fellow, Glaucoma Unit, Institute of Ophthalmology. MAJOR DEGREES: FRCS, FCOphth. First qualified in Cape Town, South Africa, in 1971. Specialist training at St Bartholomew's and Moorfields Eye Hospitals.

MUSHIN, Mr Alan S.

Especially eye problems of babies.
PRIVATE: 82 Harley Street, London W1N 1AE.
Tel: 071 780 3116.
NHS: Consultant Ophthalmic Surgeon, Royal London
Hospital, Whitechapel Road, London E1 1BB.
Tel: 071 377 7000. Fax: 071 377 7396 or 7122.
and at the Hospital for Sick Children,
34 Great Ormond Street, London WC1N 3JH.
Tel: 071 405 9200. Fax: 071 829 8643.

MAJOR DEGREES: FRCS, FCOphth. First qualified in London in 1960. Specialist training at Moorfields Eye Hospital, Royal Postgraduate Medical School and University College Hospital.

RICE, Mr Noel S. C.

Especially the cornea.
PRIVATE: 25 Wimpole Street, London W1M 7AD.
Tel: 071 935 6305. Fax: 071 436 7349.
NHS: Consultant Surgeon, Moorfields Eye Hospital,
City Road, London EC1V 2PD.
Tel: 071 253 3411. Fax: 071 253 4696.

MAJOR DEGREES: FRCS, FCOphth, MD. First qualified in Liverpool in 1967. Specialist training at St Bartholomew's and Moorfields.

SANDERS, Mr Michael D.

Especially neurological disorders of the eye.
PRIVATE: 8 Upper Wimpole Street, London W1M 7TD.
Tel: 071 935 5038.
NHS: Consultant Ophthalmologist, National Hospital,
Queen Square, London WC1N 3BG.
Tel: 071 837 3611. Fax: 071 829 8720.
and Consultant Ophthalmologist, St Thomas's Hospital,
Lambeth Palace Road, London SE1 7EH.
Tel: 071 928 9292. Fax: 071 922 8079.

DISTINCTIONS: Honorary Consultant, University of Sydney,
Australia; Civilian Consultant to the Royal Air Force. MAJOR
DEGREES: FRCP, FCOphth. First qualified in London in 1959.
Specialist training at Moorfields Eye Hospital.
USA: Lately Fellow, University of California.

SPALTON, Mr D. John.

Especially diagnosis of complex eye problems.
PRIVATE: 59 Harley Street, London W1N 1DD.
Tel: 071 935 6174.
NHS: Consultant Ophthalmic Surgeon, St Thomas's Hospital,
Lambeth Palace Road, London SE1 7EH.
Tel: 071 928 9292. Fax: 071 922 8079.

MAJOR DEGREES: FRCP, FRCS, FCOphth. First qualified in
London in 1970. Specialist training at Moorfields Eye and St
Thomas's Hospitals.

STEELE, Mr Arthur D. M.

Especially cornea, cataract and laser correction of sight.
PRIVATE: 62 Wimpole Street, London W1M 7DE.
Tel: 071 637 7400. Fax: 071 224 6216.
NHS: Consultant Ophthalmologist, Moorfields Eye Hospital,

City Road, London EC1V 2PD.
Tel: 071 253 3411. Fax: 071 253 4696.

DISTINCTIONS: *Councillor, College of Ophthalmology; editor, major recent work on cataract surgery.* MAJOR DEGREES: *FRCS, FRACO, FCOphth. First qualified in Melbourne, Australia, in 1960. Specialist training at Croydon Eye Unit and Moorfields.*

TAYLOR, Mr David S. I.

Children's eye problems.
PRIVATE: 1 Harmont House, 20 Harley Street,
London W1N 1AL. Tel: 071 935 7916. Fax: 071 323 5430.
NHS: Consultant Ophthalmologist,
Hospital for Sick Children, 34 Great Ormond Street,
London WC1N 3JH. Tel: 071 405 9200. Fax: 071 829 8643.

ACADEMIC: *Senior Lecturer, Institute of Child Health.* MAJOR DEGREES: *FRCP, FRCS, FCOphth. Specialist training at the National Hospital for Nervous Diseases, London. USA: Lately Fellow in Neuro-Ophthalmology, University of California. Member, American Association of Paediatric Ophthalmology.*

TOWNSEND, Mr Calver.

General ophthalmology.
Private: 114 Harley Street, London W1N 1AG.
Tel: 071 935 1565. Fax: 071 224 1752.
NHS: Consultant Surgeon, Western Ophthalmic Hospital,
Marylebone Road, London NW1.
Tel: 071 402 4211.

MAJOR DEGREES: *FRCS, FCOphth. First qualified in London in 1967. Specialist training at the Middlesex, Western Ophthalmic and Moorfields Eye Hospitals.*

WRIGHT, Mr John E.

Especially orbital diseases of the eye.
PRIVATE: 44 Wimpole Street, London W1M 7DG
Tel: 071 580 1251.
NHS: Consultant Ophthalmic Surgeon,
Moorfields Eye Hospital, City Road, London EC1V 2PD.
Tel: 071 253 3411. Fax: 071 253 4696.

MAJOR DEGREES: FRCS, FCOphth, MS. First qualified in Liverpool in 1956. After research in Liverpool, specialist training at Moorfields, the Royal Army Medical Corps and Western Opthalmic Hospital.

WRIGHT, Mr Peter.

PRIVATE: Refer to address and number below.
NHS: Consultant Ophthalmic Surgeon,
Moorfields Eye Hospital, City Road, London EC1V 2PD.
Tel: 071 253 3411. Fax: 071 253 4696.

ACADEMIC: Clinical Sub-Dean, Institute of Ophthalmology. DISTINCTIONS: President, College of Ophthalmology, Examiner in Ophthalmology for the Royal College of Physicians and the Royal College of Surgeons. MAJOR DEGREES: FRCS, FCOphth. First qualified in London in 1955. Specialist training at Moorfields, the Royal Air Force and King's College Hospital.

ORTHOPAEDIC SURGEONS

BENDALL, Mr Robin.

Especially hip replacement.
PRIVATE: 43 Cicada Road, London SW18 2NN.
Tel: 081 877 0742.
NHS: Consultant Orthopaedic Surgeon, St George's Hospital,
Blackshaw Road, London SW17 0QT.
Tel: 081 672 1255.

MAJOR DEGREE: FRCS. First qualified in London in 1956.
Specialist training at Charing Cross and St George's Hospitals.

BIRCH, Mr Rolfe.

Especially peripheral nerve surgery of the upper limbs, includ-
ing repair of nerve damage caused in orthopaedic surgery.
PRIVATE: 62 Wimpole Street, London W1M 7AF.
Tel: 071 935 8400.
NHS: Consultant Orthopaedic Surgeon,
Royal National Orthopaedic Hospital, Brockley Road,
Stanmore, Middlesex HA7 4LP. Tel: 081 954 2300.

MAJOR DEGREES: FRCS, MChir. First qualified in Cambridge
in 1970. Specialist training in Cambridge, at St Bartholomew's
and the Royal National Orthopaedic Hospital.

BUCKNILL, Mr Thomas M.

Especially knee injuries and complex hip replacements.
PRIVATE: 134 Harley Street, London W1N 1AH.
Tel: 071 486 2622.
NHS: Chief Consultant Surgeon in Orthopaedics,
St Bartholomew's Hospital, West Smithfield,
London EC1A 7BE. Tel: 071 601 8888. Fax: 071 601 7899.

DISTINCTIONS: Lately Surgeon Commander, Royal Navy.

MAJOR DEGREE: FRCS. First qualified in London in 1964. Specialist training at the Royal National Orthopaedic Hospital. USA: Lately Orthopaedic Clinical Research Fellow, Harvard Medical School.

CHAPMAN, Mr Robert H.

PRIVATE: 128 Harley Street, London W1N 1AH.
Tel: 071 486 9018.
NHS: Consultant Orthopaedic Surgeon, Kingston Hospital, Galsworthy Road, Kingston upon Thames, Surrey.
Tel: 081 546 7711.

MAJOR DEGREE: FRCS. First qualified in London in 1967. Specialist training at the Royal London Hospital.
USA: Lately Orthopaedic Resident, Vanderbilt University Hospital, New York.

DOWD, Mr George S. E.

Especially knees.
PRIVATE: Refer to address and number below.
NHS: Consultant Orthopaedic Surgeon,
St Bartholomew's Hospital, West Smithfield,
London EC1A 7BE. Tel: 071 601 8888. Fax: 071 601 7899.

ACADEMIC: Senior Lecturer, Institute of Orthopaedics. MAJOR DEGREES: MD, FRCS. First qualified in Liverpool in 1971. Specialist training at the Royal Liverpool Hospital.

EDGAR, Mr Michael A.

General orthopaedics, including for children.
PRIVATE: 149 Harley Street, London W1N 2DE.

Tel: 071 486 0027. Fax: 071 487 5997.
NHS: Consultant Orthopaedic Surgeon,
Middlesex Hospital, Mortimer Street, London W1N 8AA.
Tel: 071 636 8333. Fax: 071 323 0397.
and at the Royal National Orthopaedic Hospital, Brockley
Hill, Stanmore, Middlesex HA7 4LP. Tel: 081 954 2300.

DISTINCTION: *Civilian Consultant to the Royal Air Force.*
Major degrees: FRCS, MChir. Specialist training at the
Orthopaedic Hospital, Oswestry, and the Middlesex Hospital.

ENGLAND, Mr J. Patrick.

Especially the wrist.
PRIVATE: 73 Harley Street, London W1N 1DE.
Tel: 071 487 4025.
NHS: Consultant Orthopaedic Surgeon,
Hammersmith Hospital, 150 Du Cane Road,
London W12 0HS. Tel: 071 743 2030. Fax: 081 740 3169.

ACADEMIC: *Senior Lecturer in Orthopaedics, University of*
London. MAJOR DEGREE: *FRCS. First qualified in London in*
1955. Specialist training at the Royal London Hospital.

EVANS, Mr Michael J.

Private: 144 Harley Street, London W1N 1AH.
Tel: 071 935 0023.
NHS: Consultant Orthopaedic Surgeon,
Hammersmith Hospital, 150 Du Cane Road,
London W12 OHS. Tel: 071 743 2030. Fax: 081 740 3169.

ACADEMIC: *Senior Lecturer, Royal Postgraduate Medical*
School. MAJOR DEGREE: *FRCS. First qualified in Birmingham*
in 1962. Specialist training at the Royal Postgraduate Medical
School.

FIXSEN, Mr John A.

Especially congenital disorders in children, of feet, hips and spine.
PRIVATE: Refer to address and number below.
NHS: Consultant Orthopaedic Surgeon,
Hospital for Sick Children, 34 Great Ormond Street,
London WC1N 3JH. Tel: 071 405 9200. Fax: 071 829 8643.

MAJOR DEGREES: MChir, FRCS. First qualified in Cambridge in 1962. Specialist training at the Royal National Orthopaedic Hospital.

FREEMAN, Mr Roger.

The knee.
PRIVATE: 149 Harley Street, London W1N 2DE.
Tel: 071 935 4444.
NHS: Consultant Orthopaedic Surgeon, Royal London
Hospital, Whitechapel Road, London E1 1BB.
Tel: 071 377 7766.

MAJOR DEGREES: MD, FRCS. First qualified in Cambridge in 1956. Specialist training at the Middlesex and Westminster Hospitals. USA: Member, American Academy of Orthopaedic Surgeons.

HALL, Mr Anthony J.

Especially knee injuries.
PRIVATE: 126 Harley Street, London W1N 1AH.
Tel: 071 486 1096.
NHS: Consultant Orthopaedic Surgeon,
Charing Cross Hospital, Fulham Palace Road,
London W6 8RF. Tel: 071 748 2040. Fax: 081 846 1111.

ACADEMIC: Lately Postgraduate Dean, Charing Cross

Hospital. Lately Clinical Fellow in Orthopaedics, Toronto
General Hospital, Canada. DISTINCTIONS: *Honorary*
Consultant in Orthopaedics to the Royal Marsden and Queen
Charlotte's Hospitals; member, Court of Examiners, Royal
College of Surgeons. MAJOR DEGREES: *FRCS. First qualified*
in London in 1962. Specialist training at the Royal National
Orthopaedic Hospital.

HUGHES, Professor Sean P. F.

Especially infections of the bone and lumbars-spine surgery.
PRIVATE: Stamford Rooms, Hammersmith Hospital,
Du Cane Road, London W12 OHS.
Tel: 081 743 2030 Ext. 2056. Fax: 081 740 3179.
NHS AND ACADEMIC: Professor of Orthopaedic Surgery,
Hammersmith Hospital, 150 Du Cane Road,
London W12 0HS. Tel: 081 743 2030 Ext. 2056. Lately
Professor of Orthopaedics, Edinburgh.

DISTINCTIONS: *Civilian Orthopaedic surgeon to Royal Navy;*
author of standard works on orthopaedics. MAJOR DEGREES:
MS, FRCS. First qualified in London in 1966. Specialist
training at the Royal Postgraduate Medical School and the
Middlesex Hospital. USA: Research at the Mayo Clinic.

HUNT, Mr David M.

Especially knee injuries.
PRIVATE: 106 Harley Street, London W1N 1AF.
Tel: 071 935 6347.
NHS: Consultant Orthopaedic Surgeon, St Mary's Hospital,
Praed Street, London W2 1NY.
Tel: 071 262 1280 or 725 6666. Fax: 071 725 6200.

MAJOR DEGREE: *FRCS. First qualified in London in 1971.*
Specialist training at St Mary's Hospital.

IRELAND, Mr John.

Especially knee injuries.
PRIVATE: 152 Harley Street, London W1N 1HH.
Tel: 071 935 2477.
NHS: Consultant Surgeon, Department of Orthopaedics,
New King George's Hospital, Barley Lane, Goodmayes,
Essex IG3 8YB. Tel: 081 983 8000.

MAJOR DEGREE: FRCS. First qualified in London in 1966.
Specialist training at the Royal National Orthopaedic
Hospital.

JACKSON, Mr Andrew M.

Especially children, including hips and knees.
PRIVATE: 107 Harley Street, London W1N 1DG.
Tel: 071 935 9521.
NHS: Consultant in Paediatric Orthopaedics,
Queen Mary's Hospital, Roehampton, London SW15 5PN.
Tel: 081 789 6611.

DISTINCTION: Honorary Consultant Surgeon, Royal National
Orthopaedic Hospital. MAJOR DEGREE: FRCS. First qualified
in London in 1969. Specialist training at the Royal National
Orthopaedic Hospital.

JOHNSON, Mr Jonathan R.

Especially the back.
PRIVATE: 148 Harley Street, London W1N 1AH.
Tel: 071 487 5020.
NHS: Consultant Orthopaedic Surgeon, St Mary's Hospital,
Praed Street, London W2 1NY.
Tel: 071 262 1280. Fax: 071 725 6200.

MAJOR DEGREE: FRCS. First qualified in London in 1971. Specialist training at the Royal Berkshire, University College and Westminster Hospitals.

KING, Mr John B.

Sports injuries.
PRIVATE: Refer to address and number below.
NHS AND ACADEMIC: Consultant and Senior Lecturer in Orthopaedics and Trauma Surgery, Royal London Hospital, Whitechapel, London E1 1BB.
Tel: 071 377 7000. Fax: 071 377 7396 or 7122.

ACADEMIC: Director, Diploma Course in Sports Medicine, London University. MAJOR DEGREE: FRCP. First qualified in London in 1969. Specialist training at the Royal London Hospital.

LAURENCE, Mr Michael.

Rheumatoid arthritis.
PRIVATE: 106 Harley Street, London W1N 1AF.
Tel: 071 486 3131.
NHS: Consultant Orthopaedic Surgeon, Guy's Hospital, St Thomas Street, London SE1 9RT. Tel: 071 955 5000.

MAJOR DEGREE: FRCS. First qualified in London in 1953. Specialist training at St Mary's and Hammersmith Hospitals.

LOWY, Mr Martin.

Especially hip replacement.
PRIVATE: 31 Weymouth Street, London W1N 3FJ.
Tel: 071 935 1000.
NHS: Consultant Orthopaedic Surgeon, Whittington Hospital,

Highgate Hill, London N19 5NT
Tel: 071 272 3070. Fax: 071 272 6819.

MAJOR DEGREE: FRCS. First qualified in London in 1958.
Specialist training at the Royal National Orthopaedic and
Middlesex Hospitals.

MORLEY, Mr Timothy R.

The spine.
PRIVATE: 148 Harley Street, London W1N 1AH.
NHS: Royal National Orthopaedic Hospital, Brockley Hill,
Stanmore, Middlesex HA7 4LP. Tel: 081 954 2300.

MAJOR DEGREES: FRCS. First qualified in Cambridge in 1965.
Specialist training at King's College and the Royal National
Orthopaedic Hospitals.

MUIRHEAD-ALLWOOD, Mr William F. G.

Especially hip replacement.
PRIVATE: 19 Wimpole Street, London W1M 7AD
Tel: 071 935 8488. Fax: 071 636 5758.
NHS: Consultant Orthopaedic Surgeon,
Royal Northern Hospital, Holloway Road, London N7.
Tel: 071 272 7777.
and Consultant Orthopaedic Surgeon, Whittington Hospital,
Highgate Hill, London N19 5NT.
Tel: 071 272 3070. Fax: 071 272 6819.

ACADEMIC: Senior Clinical Lecturer, University of London.
DISTINCTION: Honorary Orthopaedic Consultant, St Luke's
Hospital for the Clergy. MAJOR DEGREE: FRCS. First qualified in
London in 1971. Specialist training at Westminster, University
College and Royal National Orthopaedic Hospitals.

PHILLIPS, Mr J. Barrie.

Especially orthopaedic problems of adolescence.
PRIVATE: 7 Greenhill Court, 25b Green Lane,
Northwood, Middlesex HA6 2UZ. Tel: 092 74 26948.
NHS: Consultant Orthopaedic Surgeon, Mount Vernon
Hospital, Northwood, Middlesex HA6 2RN.
Tel: 092 74 26111.

MAJOR DEGREE: FRCS. First qualified in London in 1959.
Specialist training at the John Radcliffe Infirmary, Oxford,
and the Royal National Orthopaedic Hospital.

RANSFORD, Mr Andrew O.

Especially cervical spine problems and children's spinal
deformities.
PRIVATE: 107 Harley Street, London WIN 1DG.
Tel: 071 486 1088. Fax: 071 935 5187.
NHS: Consultant Orthopaedic Surgeon, University College
Hospital, Gower Street, London WC1E 6AU.
Tel: 071 387 9300.

MAJOR DEGREE: FRCS. First qualified in Cambridge in 1966.
Specialist training at University College and the Royal
National Orthopaedic Hospital. USA: Lately Orthopaedic
Fellow, Rancho Los Amigos Hospital, Downey, California.

REYNOLDS, Mr David A.

Especially hip replacement.
PRIVATE: Churchill Clinic, 80 Lambeth Road,
London SE1 7PW. Tel: 071 620 1590.
NHS: Director, Department of Orthopaedic Surgery,
St Thomas's Hospital, Lambeth Palace Road,
London SE1 7EH. Tel: 071 928 9292. Fax: 071 922 8079.

DISTINCTION: Consultant Orthopaedic Surgeon to the Metropolitan Police. MAJOR DEGREE: FRCS. First qualified in London in 1960. Specialist training at King's College and St Thomas's. USA: Lately Associate Professor in Orthopaedics, Einstein College, New York.

ROPER, Mr Brian A.

Especially arms, shoulders, elbows, and hip replacement.
PRIVATE: 96 Harley Street, London W1N 1AF
Tel: 071 935 0856.
NHS: Consultant Orthopaedic Surgeon, Royal London Hospital, Whitechapel Road, London E1 1BB.
Tel: 071 377 7000. Fax: 071 377 7396 or 7122.

DISTINCTIONS: Honorary Consultant, Hospital for Sick Children; Court of Examiners, Royal College of Surgeons. MAJOR DEGREE: FRCS. First qualified in Oxford in 1957. Specialist training at the Royal National Orthopaedic Hospital.

SCOTT, Mr James E.

Especially backs and hip replacements.
PRIVATE: Lister Hospital, Chelsea Bridge Road, London SW1W 8RH. Tel: 071 730 3417. Fax: 071 824 8867.
NHS: Consultant Orthopaedic Surgeon, Chelsea and Westminster Hospital, 369 Fulham Road, London SW10 9NH. Tel: 081 746 8000. Fax: 081 746 8111.

MAJOR DEGREE: FRCS. First qualified in Oxford in 1968. Specialist training at the Middlesex and Royal National Orthopaedic Hospitals.

SWEETNAM, Sir Rodney.

PRIVATE: 23 Wimpole Street, London, W1M 7AD.
Tel: 071 580 5409.

DISTINCTIONS: *Consultant, Royal National Orthopaedic Hospital; Orthopaedic Surgeon to HM the Queen; Orthopaedic Consultant to the British Government and to the Royal Army Medical Corps; winner of Jacksonian Prize and Hunterian Professor, Royal College of Surgeons; Councillor, Royal College of Surgeons.* MAJOR DEGREE: *FRCS. Specialist training at the Royal National Orthopaedic and Charing Cross Hospitals.*

THOMAS, Mr E. Maelor.

Lower limbs.
PRIVATE: Churchill Clinic, 80 Lambeth Road,
London SE1 7PW. Tel: 071 928 9633.
NHS: Consultant Orthopaedic Surgeon,
King's College Hospital, Denmark Hill, London SE5 9RS.
Tel: 071 274 6222.

MAJOR DEGREE: *FRCS First qualified in London in 1957. Specialist training at the Royal Postgraduate Medical School and King's College Hospital.*

VICKERS, Mr Roger H.

Especially hip replacement and medico-legal opinions.
PRIVATE: 149 Harley Street, London W1N 1HJ.
Tel: 071 935 4444. Fax: 071 486 3782.
NHS: Consultant Orthopaedic Surgeon, St George's Hospital,
Blackshaw Road, London SW17 0QT. Tel: 081 672 1255.

MAJOR DEGREE: *FRCS. First qualified in Oxford in 1970. Specialist training at Watford General and Charing Cross Hospitals.*

WATSON, Mr Michael S.

Shoulders.
PRIVATE: 306 Emblem House, London Bridge Hospital,
27 Tooley Street, London SE1 2PR.
Tel: 071 403 5858.
NHS: Consultant Orthopaedic Surgeon, Guy's Hospital,
St Thomas Street, London SE1 9RT. Tel. 071 955 5000.

DISTINCTION: *Executive, European Society for Surgery of the Shoulder and Elbow.* MAJOR DEGREES: *MRCP, FRCS. First qualified in Cambridge in 1967. Specialist training at the Westminster and Royal National Orthopaedic Hospitals.*

PAEDIATRIC CARDIOLOGISTS

NATHAN, Dr Anthony

Especially abnormal heart rhythms.
PRIVATE: BUPA Hospital, Heathbourne Road, Bushey,
Herts WD2 1RD. Tel: 081 420 4471.
NHS: Consultant Cardiologist, St Bartholomew's Hospital,
West Smithfield, London EC1A 7BE.
Tel: 071 601 8708. Fax: 071 601 7899.

DISTINCTION: *Founding Fellow, European Society of
Cardiologists.* MAJOR DEGREES: *MD, FRCP. First qualified in
London in 1975. Specialist training at the Royal Brompton
and St Bartholomew's Hospitals.*

RIGBY, Dr Michael L.

PRIVATE: *Refer to address and number below.*
NHS: Consultant Paediatrician, Royal Brompton National
Heart and Lung Hospital, Fulham Road, London SW3 6HP.
Tel: 071 352 8121. Fax: 071 351 8099.

MAJOR DEGREE: *FRCP. First qualified in Leeds in 1970.
Specialist training at the Royal Brompton National Heart and
the Hospital for Sick Children, Toronto, Canada.*

SHINEBOURNE, Dr Elliot A.

PRIVATE: Private Consulting Rooms, Royal Brompton National
Heart and Lung Hospital, Foulis Terrace, London SW7 3LZ.
Tel: 071 352 6468.
NHS: Consultant Paediatric Cardiologist, Royal Brompton
National Heart and Lung Hospital, Fulham Road,
London SW3 6HP. Tel: 071 352 8121. Fax: 071 351 8099.

ACADEMIC: *Senior Lecturer, Heart and Lung Institute.* MAJOR

DEGREES: MD, FRCP. First qualified in London in 1970. Specialist training at St Bartholomew's and the National Heart Hospitals. USA: Lately American Heart Association Travelling Fellow in Cardiovascular Medicine.

SOMERVILLE, Dr Jane.

PRIVATE: 30 York House, Upper Montagu Street,
London W1H 1FR. Tel: 071 723 9146.
NHS: Royal Brompton National Heart and Lung Hospital,
Fulham Road, London SW3 6HP.
Tel: 071 352 8121. Fax. 071 351 8099.

ACADEMIC: Senior Lecturer, Cardiothoracic Institute; Lecturer in Paediatric Cardiology, University of Turin, Italy. MAJOR DEGREES: MD, FRCP. First qualified in London in 1955. Specialist training at the National Heart Hospital. USA: Fellow, American College of Cardiologists.

PAEDIATRIC CHEST PHYSICIAN
MATTHEW, Dr Duncan J.

PRIVATE: Refer to address and number below.
NHS: Consultant Physician, Hospital for Sick Children,
34 Great Ormond Street, London WC1N 3JH.
Tel: 071 405 9200. Fax: 071 829 8643.

*MAJOR DEGREE: FRCP. First qualified in Edinburgh in 1968.
Specialist training at the Hospital for Sick Children.*

PAEDIATRIC COLONOSCOPIST

WILLIAMS, Dr Christopher.

PRIVATE: London Clinic, 20 Devonshire Place,
London W1N 2DH. Tel: 071 935 4444. Fax: 071 486 3782.
NHS: Consultant Physician, Endoscopy Unit,
St Mark's Hospital, City Road, London EC1V 2PS.
Tel: 071 601 7919. Fax: 071 601 7973.
and the Hospital for Sick Children, 34 Great Ormond Street,
London WC1N 3JH. Tel: 071 405 9200. Fax: 071 829 8643

MAJOR DEGREE: FRCP. *First qualified in Oxford in 1964.*
Specialist training at St Mark's and St Bartholomew's
Hospitals.

PAEDIATRIC DERMATOLOGISTS

ATHERTON, Dr David J.

Especially eczema.
PRIVATE: Refer to address and number below.
NHS: Consultant Dermatologist, Hospital for Sick Children,
34 Great Ormond Street, London WC1N 3JH.
Tel: 071 405 9200. Fax: 071 829 8634.

MAJOR DEGREE: FRCP. First qualified in Cambridge in 1974.
Specialist training at Guy's Hospital and the Hospital for Sick
Children.

HARPER, Dr John I.

PRIVATE: Refer to address and number below.
NHS: Consultant Paediatric Dermatologist,
Hospital for Sick Children, 34 Great Ormond Street,
London WC1N 3JH. Tel: 071 405 9200. Fax: 071 829 8643.

MAJOR DEGREES: MD, FRCP. First qualified in 1973.

PAEDIATRIC EAR, NOSE AND THROAT SPECIALISTS

BAILEY, Mr Christian M.

PRIVATE: 55 Harley Street, London W1N 1DD.
Tel: 071 580 2426.
NHS: Consultant Surgeon, Royal National Throat, Nose and
Ear Hospital, Gray's Inn Road, London WC1X 8DA.
Tel: 071 837 8855. Fax: 071 833 5518.
and Consultant ENT Surgeon, Hospital for Sick Children,
34 Great Ormond Street, London WC1N 3JH.
Tel: 071 405 9200. Fax: 071 829 8643.

ACADEMIC: *Senior Lecturer, Institute of Laryngology and
Otology.* MAJOR DEGREE: *FRCS. First qualified in London in
1973. Specialist training at Sussex Throat and Ear Hospital
and Royal National Throat, Nose and Ear Hospital.*

BELLMAN, Dr Susan C.

Audiology.
Private: Refer to address and number below.
NHS: Hospital for Sick Children, 34 Great Ormond Street,
London WC1N 3JH. Tel: 071 405 9200. Fax: 071 829 8643.

MAJOR DEGREE: *FRCS. First qualified in Cambridge in 1972.
Specialist training at the Royal National Throat, Nose and Ear
Hospital.*

CROFT, Mr Charles B.

PRIVATE: 55 Harley Street, London W1N 1DD
Tel: 071 580 2426.
NHS: Consultant at the Royal National Throat, Nose and Ear
Hospital, Gray's Inn Road, London WC1X 8DA.
Tel: 071 837 8855. Fax: 071 833 5518.

DISTINCTIONS: Civil Consultant to the Royal Air Force; Examiner, Royal College of Surgeons, Edinburgh. MAJOR DEGREES: FRCS, DLO. First qualified (with honours) in Leeds in 1965. Specialist training at the Leeds General Infirmary. USA: Associate Professor (Otol.), Albert Einstein Medical School, New York. Diploma of the American Board of Otolaryngology.

EVANS, Mr John N. G.

Including meningitis.
PRIVATE: 55 Harley Street, London W1N 1DD.
Tel: 071 580 1481.
NHS: Consultant ENT Surgeon, St Thomas's Hospital, Lambeth Palace Road, London SE1 7EH.
Tel: 071 928 9292. Fax: 071 922 8079.
and Consultant ENT Surgeon, Hospital for Sick Children, 34 Great Ormond Street, London WC1N 3JH.
Tel: 071 405 9200.

DISTINCTION: Consultant to the Army. MAJOR DEGREE: FRCS. First qualified in London in 1959. Specialist training at the Hospital for Sick Children and St Thomas's Hospital.

MACKAY, Mr Ian S.

PRIVATE: 55 Harley Street, London W1N 1DD.
Tel: 071 580 5070.
NHS: Consultant, Royal Brompton National Heart and Lung Hospital, Fulham Road, London SW3 6HP.
Tel: 071 352 8121. Fax 071 351 8099.

MAJOR DEGREE: FRCS. First qualified in London in 1968. Specialist training at the Royal National Throat, Nose and Ear Hospital.

MAYOU, Dr Susan C.150

Children's skin problems.
PRIVATE: Refer to address and number below.
NHS: Consultant Dermatologist, Chelsea and Westminster
Hospital, 369 Fulham Road, London SW10 9NH.
Tel: 081 746 8000. Fax: 081 746 8111.

MAJOR DEGREE: MRCP. First qualified in London in 1977.
Specialist training at St Thomas's and St Bartholomew's
Hospitals.

PAEDIATRIC ENDOCRINOLOGISTS

BROOK, Professor Charles G. D.

Children's growth and development.
PRIVATE: Refer to address and number below.
NHS: Consultant Paediatrician, Middlesex Hospital,
Mortimer Street, London W1N 8AA.
Tel: 071 636 8333. Fax: 071 323 0397.

ACADEMIC: Professor of Paediatric Endocrinology, Middlesex Hospital Medical School. MAJOR DEGREES: MD, FRCP. First qualified in Cambridge in 1964. Specialist training at the Middlesex.

SAVAGE, Dr Martin.

Children's growth and development.
PRIVATE: Refer to address and number below.
NHS: Consultant Paediatric Endocrinologist,
St Bartholomew's Hospital, West Smithfield,
London EC1A 7BE. Tel: 071 601 8888. Fax: 071 601 7899.

MAJOR DEGREES: MD, FRCP. First qualified in Cambridge in 1968. Specialist training at the Hospital for Sick Children and Hôpital St Vincent de Paul, Paris.

PAEDIATRIC GASTROENTEROLOGISTS

Brueton, Dr Martin J.

Including tropical.
PRIVATE: Refer to address and number below.
NHS: Consultant Paediatrician, Chelsea and Westminster
Hospital, 369 Fulham Road, London SW10 9NH.
Tel: 081 746 8000. Fax: 081 746 8111.

*MAJOR DEGREES: MSc, MD, FRCP. First qualified in
Birmingham in 1967. Specialist training at St Bartholemew's
Hospital, London and Birmingham Children's Hospital.*

MILLA, Dr Peter J.

PRIVATE: Refer to address and number below.
NHS: Consultant Physician, Hospital for Sick Children,
34 Great Ormond Street, London WC1N 3JH.
Tel: 071 405 9200. Fax: 071 829 8643.

*MAJOR DEGREE: FRCP. First qualified in London in 1964.
Specialist training at St Bartholomew's Hospital and the
Hospital for Sick Children.*

MOWAT, Dr Alex P.

PRIVATE: 152 Harley Street, London W1N 1HH.
Tel: 071 935 8868.
NHS: Consultant Paediatrician, King's College Hospital,
Denmark Hill, London SE5 9RS.
Tel: 071 274 6222. Fax: 071 326 3589.

*MAJOR DEGREE: FRCP. First qualified in Aberdeen in 1958.
Specialist training at the Hospital for Sick Children, and the
Royal Aberdeen Children's Hospital. USA: Lately Research
Fellow, Albert Einstein College of Medicine, New York.*

WALKER-SMITH, Professor John A.

Especially diarrhoea.

PRIVATE: Refer to address and number below.

NHS: Physician in Charge, Department of Child Health,
St Bartholomew's Hospital, West Smithfield,
London EC1A 7BE: Tel: 071 601 8888. Fax: 071 601 7899.

ACADEMIC: *Professor of Paediatric Gastroenterology,
St Bartholomew's and Queen Elizabeth Hospitals.*
DISTINCTIONS: *Secretary, European Association for Paediatric
Gastroenterology. Adviser to HM Government on medical
aspects of food policy. Editorial director,* Diarrhoea Diseases
Research Journal. MAJOR DEGREES: *MD, FRCAP, FRCP. First
qualified in Sydney, Australia, in 1960. Specialist training in
Sydney, Australia, and Zurich, Switzerland.*

PAEDIATRIC HEART SURGEONS

de LEVAL, Mr Marc R.

PRIVATE: Harley Street Clinic, 35 Weymouth Street,
London W1N 4BJ. Tel: 071 935 7700.
NHS: Consultant Cardiothoracic Surgeon,
Hospital for Sick Children, 34 Great Ormond Street,
London WC1N 3JH. Tel: 071 405 9200. Fax: 071 829 8643

*MAJOR DEGREE: MD. First qualified in Liège, Belgium, in
1966.*

DEVERALL, Mr Philip B.

PRIVATE: 21 Upper Wimpole Street, London W1M 7TA.
Tel: 071 486 7753.
NHS: Consultant Cardiothoracic Surgeon, Guy's Hospital.
St Thomas Street, London SE1 9RT. Tel: 071 955 5000.

*MAJOR DEGREE: FRCS. First qualified in London in 1960.
Specialist training at the Hospital for Sick Children.
USA: Cardiovascular Research Fellow, University of Alabama.*

LINCOLN, Mr John C. R.

PRIVATE: 38 Devonshire Street, London W1N 1FW.
Tel: 071 352 6086.
NHS: Consultant Cardiothoracic Surgeon, Royal Brompton
National Heart and Lung Hospital, Fulham Road,
London SW3 6HP. Tel: 071 352 8121. Fax: 071 351 8099.

*ACADEMIC: Senior Lecturer in Paediatric Surgery,
Cardiothoracic Institute. DISTINCTION: Lately Hunterian
Professor, Royal College of Surgeons. MAJOR DEGREE: FRCS.
First qualified in Dublin in 1959. Specialist training at the
Hospital for Sick Children and the Westminster Hospital.*

USA: Lately Clinical and Research Fellow, Harvard Medical School and Massachusetts General Hospital.

STANBRIDGE, Mr Rex D. L.

PRIVATE: Refer to address and number below.
NHS: Consultant Cardiothoracic Surgeon, St Mary's Hospital, Praed Street, London W2 1NY.
Tel: 071 725 1341. Fax: 071 725 6200.

ACADEMIC: Senior Lecturer, Royal Postgraduate Medical School. MAJOR DEGREE: *FRCS. First qualified in London in 1971. Specialist training at Harefield, Hammersmith, the Middlesex Hospital and the Hospital for Sick Children. USA: Lately Research Fellow in Cardiac Surgery, University of Alabama.*

PAEDIATRIC KIDNEY SURGEON

FERNANDO, Mr Oswald N.

Kidney transplants.
PRIVATE: 152 Harley Street, London W1N 1HH.
Tel: 071 935 3834.
NHS: Consultant, Renal Transplant Surgery,
Royal Free Hospital, Pond Street, London NW3 2QG.
Tel: 071 794 0500. Fax: 071 435 5342.

ACADEMIC: *Lately Research Fellow, Royal Free Hospital.*
MAJOR DEGREE: *FRCS. First qualified in Sri Lanka in 1960.*
Specialist training at the Royal Free Hospital.

PAEDIATRIC MEDICAL ONCOLOGISTS

GOLDSTONE, Dr Anthony H.

Especially leukaemia.
PRIVATE: Portland Hospital, 209 Great Portland Street, London W1N 6AH. Tel: 071 580 4400. Fax: 071 631 1170. NHS: Consultant Haematologist, University College Hospital, Gower Street, London WC1E 6AU. Tel: 071 387 9300. Fax: 071 380 9977.

ACADEMIC: Lately Postgraduate Dean, University College Hospital Medical School. MAJOR DEGREE: FRCP. Specialist training at Addenbrooke's Hospital, Cambridge and the Cancer Research Institute.

KINGSTON, Dr Judith.

Tumours.
PRIVATE: Refer to address and number below.
NHS AND ACADEMIC: Consultant Paediatrician and Senior Lecturer, St Bartholomew's Hospital, West Smithfield, London EC1A 7BE. Tel: 071 601 8888. Fax: 071 601 7899.

MAJOR DEGREE: FRCP. First qualified in Bristol in 1973. Specialist training at the John Radcliffe Infirmary, Oxford and Addenbrooke's Hospital, Cambridge.

MALPAS, Professor James S.

PRIVATE: Refer to address and number below.
NHS: Consultant Physician, St Bartholomew's Hospital, West Smithfield, London EC1A 7BE. Tel. 071 601 8888. Fax: 071 601 7899.

ACADEMIC: Professor of Medical Oncology, Medical College of St Bartholomew's. DISTINCTIONS: Examiner to the universities of London and Oxford; Deputy-Director, Imperial Cancer Research Fund, London; Vice-President, St Bartholomew's Hospital Medical College. MAJOR DEGREES: MD, FRCP. *First qualified in London in 1955. Specialist training at the John Radcliffe Infirmary, Oxford, the Royal Postgraduate Medical School and St Bartholomew's Hospital.*

PLOWMAN, Dr P. Nicholas.

PRIVATE: 38 Harmount House, 20 Harley Street, London W1N 1AL. Tel: 071 631 1632. Fax: 071 323 3487.
NHS: Consultant Physician, Department of Radiotherapy, St Bartholomew's Hospital, West Smithfield, London EC1A 7BE. Tel: 071 601 8888. Fax: 071 601 7899.

MAJOR DEGREES: *MD, FRCP, FRCR. First qualified (with honours) in Cambridge in 1974. Specialist training at St Bartholomew's Hospital and in Cambridge.*

PRITCHARD, Dr Jon.

Blood cancers.
PRIVATE: Refer to address and number below.
NHS: Consultant Medical Oncologist, Hospital for Sick Children, 34 Great Ormond Street, London WC1N 3JH. Tel: 071 405 9200. Fax: 071 829 8643.

MAJOR DEGREE: *FRCP. First qualified in Cambridge in 1967. Specialist training at St Thomas's Hospital, London, and the Department of Haematology, University of Liverpool.*

PAEDIATRIC METABOLIC PHYSICIAN

LEONARD, Dr James V.

PRIVATE: Refer to address and number below.
NHS: Consultant Physician, Hospital for Sick Children,
34 Great Ormond Street, London WC1N 3JH.
Tel: 071 405 9200. Fax: 071 829 8643

MAJOR DEGREES: PhD, FRCP. First qualified in Cambridge in 1970. Specialist training at the Hospital for Sick Children.

PAEDIATRIC NEO-NATAL PHYSICIANS

DINWIDDIE, Dr Robert.

Respiratory disorders of the newborn.
PRIVATE: Refer to address and number below.
NHS: Consultant Paediatrician, Hospital for Sick Children,
34 Great Ormond Street, London WC1N 3JH.
Tel: 071 405 9200. Fax: 071 829 8643.

MAJOR DEGREE: FRCP. First qualified in Aberdeen in 1969.
Specialist training at the Hospital for Sick Children and the
University of Aberdeen. USA: Lately Chief Resident Physician,
Children's Hospital, Philadelphia.

HARVEY, Dr David R.

PRIVATE: Refer to address and number below.
NHS: Consultant Paediatrician, Queen Charlotte's Hospital,
Goldhawk Road, London W6 0XG.
Tel: 081 748 4666.

DISTINCTION: Consultant paediatrician to the Royal Family.
MAJOR DEGREES: FRCP. First qualified (with honours) in
London in 1960. Specialist training at the Royal Postgraduate
Medical School and the Hospital for Sick Children.

REYNOLDS, Professor Edward O. R.

PRIVATE: Refer to address and number below.
NHS AND ACADEMIC: Professor of Neo-natal Paediatrics,
University College Hospital, Gower Street, London
WC1E 6AU. Tel: 071 387 9300. Fax: 071 380 9977.

DISTINCTION: President, Neonatal Society. MAJOR DEGREES:
MD, FRCP. First qualified in London in 1958. Specialist train-
ing at St Thomas's Hospital. USA: Lately Research Fellow at
Harvard and Yale.

KOVAR, Dr Ilya.

PRIVATE: Refer to address and number below.
NHS: Consultant Paediatrician, Charing Cross Hospital,
Fulham Palace Road, London W6 8RF.
Tel: 081 846 1234. Fax: 081 846 1111.

MAJOR DEGREES: *FACP, FRCP. First qualified in Sydney,
Australia, in 1970. Specialist training in Toronto and Sydney.*

WYATT, Dr John S.

Cerebral injury in the newborn.
NHS: Consultant Paediatrician, University College Hospital,
Gower Street, London WC1E 6AU.
Tel: 071 387 9300. Fax: 071 380 9977.

ACADEMIC: *Senior Lecturer in Neo-natal Paediatrics, Rayne
Institute.* MAJOR DEGREE: *FRCP. First qualified in
London in 1978.*

PAEDIATRIC NEPHROLOGISTS

CHANTLER, Professor Cyril.

PRIVATE: Emblem House, London Bridge Hospital,
27 Tooley Street, London SE1 2PN.
Tel: 071 403 1221. Fax: 071 407 3162.
NHS: Evelina Children's Department, Guy's Hospital,
St Thomas Street, London SE1 9RT.
Tel: 071 955 5000.

*ACADEMIC: Professor of Paediatric Nephrology, Guy's
Hospital. DISTINCTION: Honorary Consultant (Paediatrics),
Guy's Hospital. MAJOR DEGREES: MD, FRCP. First qualified
in Cambridge in 1963. Specialist training at Guy's Hospital.*

DILLON, Dr Michael J.

PRIVATE: Refer to address and number below.
NHS: Consultant Physician, Hospital for Sick Children,
34 Great Ormond Street, London WC1N 3JH.
Tel: 071 405 9200. Fax: 071 829 8643.

*MAJOR DEGREE: FRCP. First qualified in London in 1962.
Specialist training at the Hospital for Sick Children.*

TROMPETER, Dr Richard S.

PRIVATE: Cromwell Hospital, Cromwell Road,
London SW5 0TU. Tel: 071 370 4233. Fax: 071 370 4063.
NHS: Consultant Paediatric Nephrologist,
Royal Free Hospital, Pond Street, London NW3 2QG.
Tel: 071 794 0500. Fax: 071 435 5342.

*ACADEMIC: Senior Lecturer in Paediatrics, Royal Free. MAJOR
DEGREE: FRCP. First qualified in London in 1970. Specialist
training at Guy's Hospital and the Hospital for Sick Children.*

PAEDIATRIC NEUROLOGISTS

ROSS, Professor Euan M.

Epilepsy.
PRIVATE: Refer to address and number below.
NHS AND ACADEMIC: Professor of Community Paediatrics,
King's College at St Giles Hospital, London SE5 7RN.
Tel: 071 708 0963. Fax: 071 701 9625.

MAJOR DEGREES: MD, FRCP. First qualified in Bristol in 1962.
Specialist training in Bristol and at Charing Cross Hospital.

WILSON, Dr John

Autism.
PRIVATE: Refer to address and number below.
NHS: Consultant Neurologist, Hospital for Sick Children,
34 Great Ormond Street, London WC1N 3JH.
Tel: 071 405 9200. Fax: 071 829 8643.

MAJOR DEGREES: PhD, FRCP. First qualified (with honours)
in Durham in 1956.

PAEDIATRIC NEUROSURGEONS

GRANT, Mr David N.

PRIVATE: Refer to address and number below.
NHS: Consultant Neurosurgeon, National Hospital,
Queen Square, London WC1N 3BG.
Tel: 071 837 3611. Fax: 071 829 8720.
and Hospital for Sick Children, 34 Great Ormond Street,
London WC1N 3JH.
Tel: 071 405 9200. Fax: 071 829 8643.

*DISTINCTION: Honorary Consultant Neurosurgeon to the
Royal Air Force. MAJOR DEGREE: FRCS. First qualified in St
Andrews in 1958. Specialist training at St Andrews, Alfred
Hospital, Melbourne, Australia; and the National Hospital.*

HAYWARD, Mr Richard D.

Especially head injuries.
PRIVATE: Refer to address and number below.
NHS: National Hospital, Queen Square,
London WC1N 3BG.
Tel: 071 837 3611. Fax: 071 829 8720.

*MAJOR DEGREE: FRCS. First qualified in London in 1966.
Specialist training at St Mary's and the National Hospitals.*

PAEDIATRIC OPHTHALMOLOGISTS

LEE, Mr John P.

Especially squints.
PRIVATE: 62 Wimpole Street, London W1M 7DE.
Tel: 071 935 5801.
NHS: Consultant Ophthalmic Surgeon,
Moorfields Eye Hospital, City Road, London EC1V 2PD.
Tel: 071 253 3411. Fax: 071 253 4696.

ACADEMIC: *Clinical Sub-Dean, Institute of Ophthalmology.*
MAJOR DEGREES: *FRCS, FCOphth. First qualified in Oxford in*
1971. Specialist training at Moorfields. USA: Fellow Paediatric
and Neuro-Ophthalmic Eye Institute, Miami.

TAYLOR, Mr David.

Especially neuro-ophthalmology.
PRIVATE: 37 Devonshire Place, London W1N 1PE.
Tel: 071 935 7916.
NHS: Consultant, Hospital for Sick Children,
34 Great Ormond Street, WC1N 3JH.
Tel: 071 405 9200. Fax: 071 829 8643.
and National Hospital for Nervous Diseases, Queen Square,
London WCIN 3BG.
Tel: 071 837 3611. Fax: 071 829 8720.

ACADEMIC: *Senior Lecturer, Institute for Child Health.* MAJOR
DEGREES: *FRCS, FRCP. First qualified in Liverpool in 1967.*
Specialist training at Moorfields Eye Hospital.
USA: Fellow in Neuro-Ophthalmology, University of
California Medical Center, San Francisco.

PAEDIATRIC ORTHOPAEDIC SURGEONS

CATERALL, Mr Anthony.

PRIVATE: 149 Harley Street, London W1N 1HG.
Tel: 071 935 4444. Fax: 071 486 3782.
NHS: Consultant, Royal National Orthopaedic Hospital,
243 Great Portland Street, London W1N 6AD.
Tel: 071 387 5070.

*MAJOR DEGREES: MChir, FRCS. First qualified in Cambridge
in 1961. Specialist training at the Royal National
Orthopaedic.*

EDGAR, Mr Michael A.

PRIVATE: 149 Harley Street, London W1N 2DE.
Tel: 071 486 0027. Fax: 071 487 5997.
NHS: Consultant Orthopaedic Surgeon, Middlesex Hospital,
Mortimer Street, London W1N 8AA.
Tel: 071 636 8333. Fax: 071 323 0397.
and the Royal National Orthopaedic Hospital, Brockley Hill,
Stanmore, Middlesex, HA7 4LP.Tel: 081 954 2300.

*DISTINCTION: Civilian Consultant to the Royal Air Force.
MAJOR DEGREES: FRCS, MChir. Specialist training at the
Orthopaedic Hospital, Oswestry, and the Middlesex Hospital.*

FIXSEN, Mr John A.

Especially congenital disorders of feet, hips and spine.
PRIVATE: Refer to address and number below.
NHS: Consultant Orthopaedic Surgeon,
Hospital for Sick Children, 34 Great Ormond Street,
London WC1N 3JH. Tel: 071 405 9200. Fax: 071 829 8643.

MAJOR DEGREES: MChir, FRCS. First qualified in Cambridge

in 1962. Specialist training at the Royal National Orthopaedic Hospital.

HUNT, Mr David M.

Especially birth injuries.
PRIVATE: 106 Harley Street, London W1N 1AF.
Tel: 071 935 6347.
NHS: Consultant Orthopaedic Surgeon, St Mary's Hospital, Praed Street, London W2 1NY.
Tel: 071 262 1280. Fax: 071 725 6200.

MAJOR DEGREE: FRCS. First qualified in London in 1971. Specialist training at St Mary's.

JACKSON, Mr Andrew M.

Injuries to ankles and chests, and inbalance in children.
PRIVATE: 107 Harley Street, London W1N 1BG.
Tel: 071 935 9521.
NHS: Consultant Orthopaedic Surgeon, University College Hospital, Gower Street, London WC1E 6AU.
Tel: 071 387 9300. Fax: 071 380 9977.
Consultant Surgeon, Hospital for Sick Children, 34 Great Ormond Street, London WC1N 3JH. Tel: 071 405 9200.

DISTINCTION: Honorary Consultant Surgeon, Royal National Orthopaedic Hospital. MAJOR DEGREE: FRCS. First qualified in London in 1969. Specialist training at the Royal National Orthopaedic Hospital.

RANSFORD, Mr Andrew O.

Especially peripheral nervous surgery of the spine.
PRIVATE: 107 Harley Street, London W1N 1DG.

Tel: 071 486 1088.
NHS: Consultant Orthopaedic Surgeon, University College
Hospital, Gower Street, London WC1E 6AU.
Tel: 071 387 9300. Fax: 071 380 9977.
and Consultant Orthopaedic Surgeon,
Royal National Orthopaedic Hospital, 45/51 Bolsover Street,
London W1N 6AD. Tel: 071 387 5070.

First qualified in Cambridge in 1966. Specialist training at
University College and the Royal National Orthopaedic
Hospital. USA: Lately Orthopaedic Fellow, Rancho Los
Amigos Hospital, Downey, California.

WEBB, Mr Peter J.

Especially scoliosis.
PRIVATE: 134 Harley Street, London W1N 1AH.
Tel: 071 487 2819.
NHS: Consultant Orthopaedic Surgeon,
Hospital for Sick Children, 34 Great Ormond Street,
London WC1N 3JH. Tel: 071 405 9200. Fax: 071 829 8643.

MAJOR DEGREE: FRCS. First qualified in London in 1969.
Specialist training at the Royal National Orthopaedic and the
Hospital for Sick Children.

PAEDIATRIC PLASTIC SURGEONS

BOWEN, Mr John E.

PRIVATE: Flat 1, 30 Harley Street, London W1N 1AB.
Tel: 071 636 0955.
NHS: Honorary Consultant Plastic Surgeon, Queen Victoria
Hospital, East Grinstead, West Sussex. Tel: 0342 410210

*MAJOR DEGREE: FRCS. First qualified in Cambridge in 1962.
Specialist training at St Thomas's Hospital, the Hospital for
Sick Children, and Queen Victoria Hospital.*

COLLIN, Mr L. Richard.

Especially plastic and reconstructive surgery of the eyelids.
PRIVATE: 67 Harley Street, London W1N 1DE.
Tel: 071 486 2699.
NHS: Consultant Surgeon, Moorfields Eye Hospital,
City Road, London EC1V 2PD
Tel: 071 253 2411. Fax: 071 253 4696.

*ACADEMIC: Senior Lecturer, Institute of Ophthalmology;
Secretary, European Society of Ophthalmic Plastic and
Reconstructive Surgery. DISTINCTION: Consultant Ophthalmic
Surgeon, Hospital for Sick Children. MAJOR DEGREES: FRCS,
FCOphth. First qualified in Cambridge in 1968. Specialist
training at Moorfields Eye Hospital. USA: Lately Fellow in
Ophthalmic Plastic and Reconstructive Surgery, University of
California Medical School, San Francisco.*

JONES, Mr Barry M.

Especially hands and faces.
PRIVATE: 14a Upper Wimpole Street, London W1.
Tel: 071 935 1938.
NHS : Consultant Plastic and Reconstructive Surgeon,

Hospital for Sick Children, Great Ormond Street,
London WC1N 3JH: Tel: 071 405 9200. Fax: 071 829 8643.

*MAJOR DEGREES: MS, FRCS. First qualified in London in
1974. Specialist training at Mount Vernon Hospital,
Northwood and Charing Cross Hospital Medical School.*

SANDERS, Mr Roy.

PRIVATE: Consulting Suite, 82 Portland Place,
London, W1N 3DH. Tel: 071 580 3541.
NHS: Consultant Plastic Surgeon, Mount Vernon Hospital,
Northwood, Middlesex HA6 2RN. Tel: 092 74 26111.

*ACADEMIC: Honorary Senior Lecturer, University of London.
MAJOR DEGREE: FRCS. First qualified (with honours in
anatomy) in London 1962. Specialist training at
St Bartholomew's Hospital. Lately Surgeon in Charge,
Rainsford Mowlem Burns Centre.*

SMITH, Mr Paul J.

Especially hands.
PRIVATE: 48 Wimpole Street, London W1M 7DG.
Tel: 071 486 9500.
NHS: Consultant Plastic Surgeon, Hospital for Sick Children,
34 Great Ormond Street, London WC1N 3JH.
Tel: 071 405 9200. Fax: 071 829 8643.

*DISTINCTIONS: First prize, American Association of Hand
Surgery; Pulvertaft Prize, British Society of Surgery of the
Hand. MAJOR DEGREE: FRCS. First qualified in Newcastle in
1968. USA: Visiting Professor, Plastic Surgery,
Salt Lake City, Utah.*

PAEDIATRIC SURGEONS

BRERETON, Mr Roger J.

PRIVATE: Refer to address and number below.
NHS: Consultant Paediatric Surgeon, Chelsea and
Westminster Hospital, 369 Fulham Road,
London SW10 9NH. Tel: 081 746 8000. Fax: 081 746 8111.

*MAJOR DEGREE: FRCS. First qualified in Liverpool in 1966.
Specialist training at Alderhay Hospital, Liverpool, and the
Hospital for Sick Children.*

DAWSON, Mr John.

PRIVATE: 73 Harley Street, London W1N 1DE.
Tel: 071 935 5385.
NHS AND ACADEMIC: Dean of Clinical Medicine,
King's College Hospital, Denmark Hill, London SE5 9RS.
Tel: 071 274 6222. Fax: 071 326 3582.

*DISTINCTIONS: Lately Surgeon to HM the Queen; Examiner,
Royal College of Surgeons; Vice-Chairman, British Journal of
Surgeons. MAJOR DEGREES: MS, FRCS. First qualified (with
honours) in London in 1955. Specialist training at Oxford,
St James's and King's College Hospitals. USA: Lately
Harvard Surgical Unit, Boston.*

KIELY, Mr Edward M.

Neo-natal surgery.
PRIVATE: Refer to address and number below.
NHS: Hospital for Sick Children, 34 Great Ormond Street,
London WC1N 3JH.
Tel: 071 405 9200. Fax: 071 829 8643.

MAJOR DEGREE: FRCS. First qualified in Ireland in 1968.

Specialist training at the Hospital for Sick Children and the Children's Hospital, Birmingham.

MADDEN, Mr Nicholas P.

PRIVATE: Refer to address and number below.
NHS: Consultant Paediatric Surgeon,
Chelsea and Westminster Hospital, 369 Fulham Road,
London SW10 9NH. Tel: 081 746 8000. Fax: 081 746 8111.

MAJOR DEGREE: FRCS. First qualified in Oxford in 1974. Specialist training at Leeds General Infirmary.

SPITZ, Professor Lewis.

Including separation of Siamese twins.
PRIVATE: Refer to address and number below.
NHS: Consultant Surgeon, Hospital for Sick Children,
34 Great Ormond Street, London WC1N 3JH.
Tel: 071 242 9789. Fax: 071 829 8643.

ACADEMIC: Nuffield Professor of Paediatric Surgery, Institute of Child Health. MAJOR DEGREES: PhD, FRCS. First qualified in Pretoria, South Africa, in 1963.

PAEDIATRIC TROPICAL PHYSICIAN

TOMKINS, Professor Andrew M.

PRIVATE: Refer to address and number below.
NHS: Consultant Physician, Hospital for Sick Children,
34 Great Ormond Street, London WC1N 3JH.
Tel: 071 405 9200. Fax: 071 829 8643.

ACADEMIC: *Professor of International Child Health, Institute of Child Health.* MAJOR DEGREE: *FRCP. First qualified in London in 1966. Specialist training in Nigeria and The Gambia.*

PAEDIATRIC UROLOGISTS

DUFFY, Mr Patrick G.

PRIVATE: Refer to address and number below.
NHS: Hospital for Sick Children, 34 Great Ormond Street,
London WC1N 3JH.
Tel: 071 405 9200. Fax: 071 829 8643.

ACADEMIC: *Senior Lecturer in Paediatric Urology, Institute of Urology. MAJOR DEGREE: FRCSI. First qualified in Belfast in 1973.*

RANSLEY, Mr Philip G.

PRIVATE: Refer to address and number below.
NHS: Consultant Urological Surgeon,
Hospital for Sick Children, 34 Great Ormond Street,
London WC1N 3JH.
Tel: 071 405 9200. Fax: 071 829 8643.

ACADEMIC: *Senior Lecturer in Paediatric Urology, Institute of Child Health. MAJOR DEGREE: FRCS. First qualified in Cambridge in 1967. Specialist training at the Hospital for Sick Children and St Peter's.*

PAIN RELIEF PHYSICIANS

FOSTER, Dr James M. G.

PRIVATE: Princess Grace Hospital, 42 Nottingham Place, London W1N 3FD. Tel: 071 486 1234.
NHS: Consultant, Pain Clinic, St Bartholomew's Hospital, West Smithfield, London EC1A 7BE.
Tel: 071 601 8888. Fax: 071 601 7899.

DISTINCTION: Visiting Consultant, St Joseph's Hospice. MAJOR DEGREE: FFARCS. First qualified in London in 1974. Specialist training in Perth, Western Australia, and at Guy's Hospital.

GALLAGHER, Dr Wendy J.

PRIVATE: Refer to address and number below.
NHS: Consultant, Pain Clinic, St Bartholomew's Hospital, West Smithfield, London EC1A 7BE.
Tel: 071 601 8888. Fax: 071 601 7899.

MAJOR DEGREE: FFARCS. First qualified in London in 1980.

JUSTINS, Dr Douglas M.

PRIVATE: Refer to address and number below.
NHS: Consultant, Pain Management Unit, St Thomas's Hospital, Lambeth Palace Road, London SE1 7EH. Tel: 071 928 9292. Fax: 071 922 8079.

MAJOR DEGREE: FFARCS. First qualified in Australia in 1970.

MANN, Dr Felix B.

Acupuncture – pioneer of in Britain.
PRIVATE: 15 Devonshire Place, London W1 1PB.
Tel: 071 935 7575.
NHS: None

DISTINCTION: *Founder, lately President, Medical Acupuncture Society. First qualified in Cambridge in 1955. Specialist training at the Westminster Hospital, London, and in Heidelberg, Germany and Strasbourg, France.*

NAYSMITH, Dr Anne.

PRIVATE: Refer to address and number below.
NHS: Consultant Physician in Palliative Medicine,
St Mary's Hospital, Praed Street, London W2 1NY
Tel: 071 262 1280 or 725 6666. Fax: 071 725 6200.

MAJOR DEGREE: *FRCP. First qualified in Edinburgh in 1971. Specialist training at Edinburgh Royal Infirmary and the Middlesex Hospital.*

PITHER, Dr Charles E.

Including regional anaesthesia.
PRIVATE: Refer to address and number below.
NHS: Consultant, Pain Management Unit,
St Thomas's Hospital, Lambeth Palace Road,
London SE1 7EH. Tel: 071 928 9292. Fax: 071 922 8079.

MAJOR DEGREE: *FFARCS. First qualified in London in 1977. Specialist training at St Thomas's. USA: Fellow, Anaesthesia and Pain Control Unit, University of Cincinnati, Ohio.*

WEDLEY, Dr John R.

PRIVATE: Emblem House, London Bridge Hospital,
27 Tooley Street, London SE1 2PR.
Tel: 071 403 3876. Fax: 071 407 3162.
NHS: Consultant, Pain Relief Clinic, Guy's Hospital,
St Thomas Street, London SE1 9RT. Tel: 071 955 5000.

MAJOR DEGREE: FFARCS. *First qualified in Liverpool in 1968.*
Specialist training at Guy's Hospital.

PANCREATIC SURGEONS

GLAZER, Mr Geoffrey

PRIVATE: Humana Hospital Wellington, 8A Wellington Place, London NW8 9LE. Tel: 071 586 5959. Fax: 071 586 1960. NHS: Consultant Surgeon, St Mary's Hospital, Praed Street, London W2 1NY. Tel: 071 262 1280 or 725 6666. Fax: 071 725 6200.

MAJOR DEGREES: MS, FRCS, FACS. First qualified in London in 1964. Specialist training at St Mary's Hospital.

KNIGHT, Mr Michael J.

Including in relation to diabetes.
Private: 135 Harley Street, London W1N 1DJ.
Tel: 071 487 3501.
NHS: Consultant Surgeon, St George's Hospital,
Blackshaw Road, London SW17 0QT. Tel: 081 672 1255.

ACADEMIC: Senior Lecturer, St George's Hospital Medical School. DISTINCTIONS: Lately Hunterian Professor, Royal College of Surgeons; lately President, Pancreatic Society. MAJOR DEGREES: MS, FRCS. First qualified in London in 1963. Specialist training at St George's. USA: Surgical Research Fellow, Washington University, St Louis, Missouri.

RUSSELL, Mr R. Christopher.

PRIVATE: 149 Harley Street, London W1N 1HG.
Tel: 071 486 1164. Fax: 071 487 5997.
NHS: Consultant Surgeon, Middlesex Hospital, Mortimer Street,
London W1N 8AA. Tel: 071 636 8333. Fax: 071 323 0397.

MAJOR DEGREES: MS, FRCS. First qualified in London in 1963. Specialist training at St Mary's and Central Middlesex Hospitals.

PLASTIC SURGEONS

BOWEN, Mr John E.

Including children.
PRIVATE: Flat 1, 30 Harley Street, London W1N 1AB.
Tel: 071 636 0955.
NHS: Honorary Consultant Plastic Surgeon,
Queen Victoria Hospital, East Grinstead, West Sussex.
Tel: 0342 410210.

MAJOR DEGREE: FRCS. First qualified in Cambridge in 1962.
Specialist training at St Thomas's Hospital, and the Hospital
for Sick Children, and Queen Victoria Hospital, East
Grinstead.

BREACH, Mr Nicholas M.

Reconstruction of head and neck.
PRIVATE: 82 Portland Place, London W1N 3DH.
Tel: 071 636 1298.
NHS: Consultant Reconstructive Surgeon, Royal Marsden
Hospital, Fulham Road, London SW3 6JJ.
Tel: 071 352 8171. Fax: 071 351 3785.

MAJOR DEGREES: FRCS, FDS. First qualified in London in
1970. Specialist training at Queen Victoria Hospital, East
Grinstead, where he was lately Director of the Burns Centre.

BROUGH, Mr Michael D.

Private: Consulting Suite, 82 Portland Place,
London W1N 3DH. Tel: 071 935 8910.
NHS: Consultant Plastic Surgeon, University College Hospital,
Gower Street, London WC1E 6AU.
Tel: 071 387 9300. Fax: 071 380 9977.

MAJOR DEGREE: FRCS. First qualified in Cambridge in 1968.

*Specialist training at Queen Elizabeth Hospital for Children
and Whipp's Cross Hospital.*

CLARKE, Mr John A.

Especially burns.
PRIVATE: Refer to address and number below.
NHS: Consultant in Charge, Burns Unit,
Queen Mary's Hospital, Roehampton, London SW15 5PN.
Tel: 081 789 6611.

MAJOR DEGREE: FRCS. First qualified in London in 1963.

COLLIN, Mr L. Richard.

*Especially plastic and reconstructive surgery of the eyelids,
etc., including for children.*
PRIVATE: 67 Harley Street, London W1N 1DE.
Tel: 071 486 2699.
NHS: Consultant Surgeon, Moorfields Eye Hospital,
City Road, London EC1V 2PD
Tel: 071 253 2411. Fax: 071 253 4696.

*DISTINCTIONS: Consultant Ophthalmic Surgeon, Hospital for
Sick Children, Great Ormond Street. ACADEMIC: Senior
Lecturer, Institute of Ophthalmology; Secretary, European
Society of Ophthalmic Plastic and Reconstructive Surgery.
MAJOR DEGREES: FRCS, FCOphth. First qualified in
Cambridge in 1968. Specialist training at Moorfields Eye
Hospital. USA: Lately Fellow in Ophthalmic Plastic and
Reconstructive Surgery, University of California Medical
School, San Francisco.*

DAVIES, Mr David M.

Rheumatoid and carpel tunnel. Breast reconstruction.
PRIVATE: 55 Harley Street, London W1N 1DD.
Tel: 071 631 3927.
NHS: Consultant Plastic Surgeon, Chelsea and Westminster
Hospital, 369 Fulham Road, London SW10 9NH.
Tel: 081 746 8000. Fax: 081 746 8111.

ACADEMIC: *Senior Lecturer, Royal Postgraduate Medical
School. Lately Research Fellow, Queen Victoria Hospital, East
Grinstead and the Royal Melbourne Hospital, Australia.
MAJOR DEGREE: FRCS. First qualified in London in 1970.
Specialist training at Queen Victoria Hospital, East Grinstead.*

DAVIS, Mr Peter K. B.

PRIVATE: 97 Harley Street, London W1N 1DF.
Tel: 071 486 4976.
NHS: Consultant Plastic Surgeon, St Thomas's Hospital,
Lambeth Palace Road, London SE1 7EH.
Tel: 071 928 9292. Fax: 071 922 8079.

DISTINCTION: *Lately President, British Association of
Aesthetic Plastic Surgeons. MAJOR DEGREES: FRCS, MS. First
qualified in 1969. Specialist training at Leicester General
Hospital and in Oxford.*

EVANS, Mr David.

Hands.
PRIVATE: Hand Clinic, Oakley Green, Windsor, Berkshire.
Tel: 0753 831333.
NHS: Consultant Plastic Surgeon, Wexham Park Hospital,
Slough, Berkshire. Tel: 0753 633000.

MAJOR DEGREE: *FRCS. First qualified in London in 1965.
Specialist training at Churchill Hospital, Oxford.*

GAULT, Mr David.

Ear reconstruction.
PRIVATE: Refer to address and number below.
NHS: Consultant Plastic Surgeon, St Thomas's Hospital,
Lambeth Palace Road, London SE1 7EH
Tel: 071 928 9292. Fax: 071 922 8079.

MAJOR DEGREE: FRCS. First qualified in Edinburgh in 1977.
Specialist training at the Royal Infirmary, Edinburgh, and St
Thomas's Hospital.

HARRISON, Mr Douglas H.

Facial paralysis.
PRIVATE: Flat 33, Harmont House, 20 Harley Street,
London W1N 1AA. Tel: 071 935 6184.
NHS: Consultant Plastic Surgeon, Mount Vernon Hospital,
Northwood, Middlesex HA6 2RN. Tel: 092 742 6111.

DISTINCTION: Lately Hunterian Professor, Royal College of
Surgeons. MAJOR DEGREE: FRCS. First qualified in London in
1967. Specialist training in Edinburgh and at Mount Vernon.

JONES, Mr Barry M.

Craniofacial surgery.
PRIVATE: 14a Upper Wimpole Street, London W1.
Tel: 071 935 1938.
NHS: Consultant Plastic and Reconstructive Surgeon,
Hospital for Sick Children, 34 Great Ormond Street,
London WC1N 3JH. Tel: 071 405 9200. Fax: 071 829 8643.

ACADEMIC: Research Fellow Hôpital des Enfants Malades,
Paris, and Charing Cross Hospital Medical School, London.
MAJOR DEGREES: FRCS, MS. First qualified in London in
1974. Specialist training at Mount Vernon Hospital,
Northwood.

MAYOU, Mr Brian J.

Including reduction of stomachs.
PRIVATE: Lister Hospital, Chelsea Bridge Road, London SW1
W8RH. Tel: 071 730 7951. Fax: 071 824 8867.
NHS: Consultant Plastic Surgeon, St Thomas's Hospital,
Lambeth Palace Road, London SE1 7EH.
Tel: 071 928 9292. Fax: 071 922 8079.

MAJOR DEGREE: FRCS. First qualified in Birmingham in 1969.
Specialist training at Mount Vernon Hospital, Northwood,
and the Hospital for Sick Children.

MORGAN, Mr Brian D. G.

Skin cancer.
PRIVATE: Private Consulting Rooms, University College
Hospital, Grafton Way, London WC1E 6AU.
Tel: 071 387 8323. Fax: 071 380 9977.
NHS: Consultant Plastic Surgeon, University College Hospital,
Gower Street, London WC1E 6AU.
Tel: 071 387 9300. Fax: 071 380 9977.

DISTINCTION: Court of Examiners, Royal College of Surgeons.
MAJOR DEGREE: FRCS. First qualified in London in 1959.
Specialist training at University College Hospital, and
Mount Vernon Hospital, Northwood.

NICOLLE, Mr Frederick V.

PRIVATE: 30 Harley Street, London W1N 1AB.
Tel: 071 637 9595.

ACADEMIC: Lately Lecturer, Royal Postgraduate Medical
School. DISTINCTIONS: A founder of the British Association of
Aesthetic Plastic Surgeons. MAJOR DEGREES: FRCS, MChir.
First qualified in Cambridge in 1957. Specialist training at the

Royal Postgraduate Medical School, and Montreal General Hospital, Canada. Lately Consultant Plastic Surgeon, Hammersmith Hospital. USA: Member, American Society of Plastic and Reconstructive Surgeons.

SANDERS, Mr Roy.

PRIVATE: Consulting Suite, 82 Portland Place, London W1N 3DH. Tel: 071 580 3541.
NHS: Consultant Plastic Surgeon, Mount Vernon Hospital, Northwood, Middlesex HA6 2RN. Tel: 092 74 26111.

ACADEMIC: *Honorary Senior Lecturer, University of London.* DISTINCTIONS: *Lately, Visiting Professor, universities of Genoa, Italy, Hong Kong and Bombay, India.* MAJOR DEGREE: *FRCS. First qualified (with honours in anatomy) in London in 1962. Specialist training at St Bartholomew's Hospital. Lately Surgeon in Charge, Rainsford Mowlem Burns Centre.*

SMITH, Mr Paul J.

Especially children's hands.
PRIVATE: 48 Wimpole Street, London W1M 7DG.
Tel: 071 486 9500.
NHS: Consultant Plastic Surgeon, Hospital for Sick Children, 34 Great Ormond Street, London WC1N 3JH.
Tel: 071 405 9200. Fax: 071 829 8643.

DISTINCTIONS: *Fist prize, American Association of Hand Surgery; Pulvertaft Prize, British Society of Surgery of the Hand.* MAJOR DEGREE: *FRCS. First qualified in Newcastle in 1968. USA: Visiting Professor, Plastic Surgery, Salt Lake City, Utah.*

WARD, Mr Christopher

PRIVATE: Royal Masonic Hospital, Ravenscourt Park,
London W6 0TN. Tel: 081 748 4611.
NHS: Consultant Plastic and Reconstructive Surgeon,
Charing Cross Hospital, Fulham Palace Road,
London W6 8RF. Tel: 081 846 1234. Fax: 081 846 1111.

ACADEMIC: *Lately Clinical Research Fellow in Plastic Surgery,
Hospital for Sick Children, Toronto, Canada.* MAJOR DEGREE:
*FRCS. First qualified in London in 1966. Specialist training at
the Royal Postgraduate Medical School.*

WATERHOUSE, Mr Norman.

Cleft lip and palate.
PRIVATE: 55 Harley Street, London W1N 1DD.
Tel: 071 636 4073.
NHS: Consultant Plastic Surgeon, Charing Cross Hospital,
Fulham Palace Road, London W6 8RF.
Tel: 081 846 1234. Fax: 081 846 1111.

MAJOR DEGREE: *FRCS. First qualified in Birmingham in 1978.
Specialist training at Mount Vernon Hospital, Northwood,
and the Cranio-Facial Unit, Adelaide, Australia.*

WHITFIELD, Mr Patrick J.

Especially remodelling of professional models and actresses.
PRIVATE: 17 Harley Street, London W1N 1DA.
Tel: 071 580 6283.
NHS: Consultant Plastic Surgeon, Queen Mary's Hospital,
Roehampton, London SW15 5PN. Tel: 081 789 6611.

DISTINCTION: *A founder of the British Association of Aesthetic
Plastic Surgeons.* MAJOR DEGREE: *FRCS. First qualified in
London in 1958. Specialist training at Queen Mary's Hospital,
Roehampton, and in Paris, Rome and New York.*

PSYCHIATRISTS

BOWDEN, Dr Paul M.A.

Forensic psychiatry: for mentally abnormal offenders.
PRIVATE: Refer to address and number below.
NHS: Consultant Forensic Psychiatrist, Maudsley Hospital,
Denmark Hill, London SE5 8AZ
Tel: 071 703 6333. Fax: 071 703 0179.

MAJOR DEGREES: MPhil, FRCP, FRCPsych. First qualified in London in 1965. Specialist training at Royal Postgraduate Medical School.

CHRISTIE-BROWN, Dr Jeremy R. W.

Including psychiatric aspects of the menopause.
PRIVATE: 130 Harley Street, London W1N 1AH.
Tel: 071 935 2190.
NHS: Consultant Psychiatrist, Maudsley Hospital,
Denmark Hill, London SE5 8AZ.
Tel: 071 703 6333. Fax: 071 703 0179.

MAJOR DEGREES: FRCP, FRCPsych. First qualified in Oxford in 1960. Specialist training at the Middlesex and Maudsley Hospitals.

COX, Dr Murray.

Especially psychotherapy in forensic treatment.
PRIVATE: London Independent Hospital, 1 Beaumont Square,
Stepney Green, London E1 4NL.
Tel: 071 790 7845. Fax: 071 265 9032.
NHS: Consultant Psychiatrist, Broadmoor Hospital,
Crowthorne, Berks RG11 7EG. Tel: 0344 773111.

MAJOR DEGREE: FRCPsych. First qualified in Cambridge in 1956. Specialist training at the Royal London Hospital.

CROWE, Dr Michael J.

Especially marital, sexual and family therapy.
PRIVATE: 21 Wimpole Street, London W1M 7AD.
Tel: 071 637 0146.
NHS: Consultant Psychiatrist, Maudsley Hospital,
Denmark Hill, London SE5 8AZ.
Tel: 071 703 6333. Fax: 071 703 0179.

MAJOR DEGREES: *MPhil, DM, FRCP, FRCPsych. First qualified in Oxford in 1963. Specialist training at Addenbrooke's
Hospital, Cambridge, and the Maudsley Hospital.*

CROWN, Dr Sidney.

Especially psychotherapy.
PRIVATE: 14 Devonshire Place, London W1N 1PB.
Tel: 071 935 0640.
NHS: Consultant Psychiatrist, Royal London Hospital,
Whitechapel Road, London E1 1BB.
Tel: 071 377 7000. Fax: 071 377 7396 or 7122.

MAJOR DEGREES: *PhD, FRCP, FRCPsych. First qualified in
London in 1959. Specialist training at the Middlesex and
National Hospitals.*

FRY, Dr Anthony H.

Especially stress.
PRIVATE: Emblem House, London Bridge Hospital, 27 Tooley
Street, London SE1 2PR.
Tel: 071 607 3937. Fax: 071 407 3162.
NHS: Consultant Physician, Department of Psychological
Medicine, Guy's Hospital, St Thomas Street,
London SE1 9RT. Tel: 071 955 5000.

DISTINCTIONS: *Medical Adviser, National Marriage Guidance*

Council. *Examiner, Royal College of Psychiatrists.*
MAJOR DEGREE: *FRCPsych. First qualified in London
in 1966. Specialist training at the Middlesex and Maudsley
Hospitals.*

GREENWOOD, Dr Monica H.

Old age.
PRIVATE: 144 Harley Street, London W1N 1AH.
Tel: 071 935 0023.
NHS: Consultant Psychiatrist, Middlesex Hospital,
Mortimer Street, London W1N 8AA.
Tel: 071 636 8333. Fax: 071 323 0397.

MAJOR DEGREE: *FRCPsych. First qualified in 1967 in London.
Specialist training at the Royal Free Hospital, London and the
Shenley Hospital, Radlett.*

HAILSTONE, Dr J. Donovan.

Especially psychiatric disorders of doctors.
PRIVATE: 130 Harley Street, London W1N 1AH.
NHS: Consultant Physician in Psychological Medicine,
Royal Free Hospital, Pond Street, London NW3 2QG.
Tel: 071 794 0500. Fax: 071 435 5342.

MAJOR DEGREE: *FRCPsych. First qualified in London in 1961.
Specialist training at St Mary's Hospital. USA: Lately Resident
in Psychiatry, Boston State Hospital, Massachusetts.*

HIRSCH, Professor Stephen R.

Especially schizophrenia.
PRIVATE: 20 Mansel Road, London SW19 4AA.
Tel: 081 944 0308.
NHS: Consultant Psychiatrist, Charing Cross Hospital,
Fulham Palace Road, London W6 8RF.

ACADEMIC: *Professor of Psychiatry, Charing Cross and
Westminster Medical School.* DISTINCTION: *Lately President,
Psychiatric Section, Royal Society of Medicine.* MAJOR
DEGREES: *MD, FRCP, FRCPsych. First qualified in Baltimore,
USA, in 1963. Specialist training at Johns Hopkins, Baltimore,
and Westminster Hospital.*

ISAACS, Dr Anthony D.

General psychiatry.
PRIVATE: 138 Harley Street, London W1N 1AH.
Tel: 071 935 1963. Fax: 071 935 0554.
NHS: Consultant Psychiatrist, Maudsley Hospital,
Denmark Hill, London SE5 8AZ.
Tel: 071 703 6333. Fax: 071 703 0179.

ACADEMIC: *Sub-Dean, Institute of Psychiatry.* MAJOR DEGREES:
*FRCP, FRCPsych. First qualified in London in 1954.
Specialist training at the Maudsley Hospital.*

KING, Dr Michael B.

*Psychological aspects of AIDS, and of male victims of sexual
abuse.*
PRIVATE: Refer to address and number below.
NHS: Consultant Psychiatrist, Royal Free Hospital, Pond
Street, London NW3 2QG.
Tel: 071 794 0500. Fax: 071 435 5342.

ACADEMIC: Senior Lecturer, Institute of Psychiatry. MAJOR DEGREES: MD, FRCPsych. First qualified in New Zealand in 1976. Specialist training in Auckland and at the Royal Free Hospital.

LADER, Professor Malcolm H.

Pharmaceutical treatment of mental illness.
PRIVATE: Refer to address and number below.
NHS: Consultant Psychiatrist, Maudsley Hospital,
Denmark Hill, London SE5 8AZ.
Tel: 071 703 6333. Fax: 071 703 0179.

ACADEMIC: Professor of Clinical Psychopharmacology, Institute of Psychiatry. MAJOR DEGREES: MD, FRCPsych. First qualified in London in 1959. Specialist training at the Maudsley Hospital.

LEVY, Professor Raymond.

Alzheimer's disease.
PRIVATE: Refer to address and number below.
NHS: Consultant Psychiatrist, Maudsley Hospital,
Denmark Hill, London SE5 8AZ.
Tel: 071 703 6333. Fax: 071 703 0179.

ACADEMIC: Professor of Old Age Psychiatry, Institute of Psychiatry. MAJOR DEGREES: FRCP, FRCPsych. First qualified in Edinburgh in 1957.

LIPSEDGE, Dr Maurice S.

Especially cross-cultural problems.
PRIVATE: Keats House, 24 St Thomas Street, London SE1 9RT.
Tel: 071 407 7517.

NHS: Consultant in Psychological Medicine, Guy's Hospital, St Thomas Street, London SE1 9RT. Tel: 071 955 5000.

DISTINCTIONS: *Councillor, Association of University Teachers in Psychiatry. Lately Psychiatric Adviser, Alcoholics Recovery Project. MAJOR DEGREES: FRCP, FRCPsych. First qualified in London in 1966. Specialist training at St Bartholomew's Hospital.*

LLOYD, Dr Jeffrey G.

Private: 148 Harley Street, London W1N 1AH.
Tel: 071 935 1207.
NHS: Consultant Psychiatrist, Royal Free Hospital,
Pond Street, London NW3 2QG.
Tel: 071 794 0500. Fax: 071 435 5342.

DISTINCTION: *Editor,* Journal of Psychosomatic Research.
MAJOR DEGREES: *MPhil, MD, FRCP, FRCPsych. First quali-fied in Cambridge in 1967. Specialist training at the Maudsley Hospital.*

MACKEITH, Dr James A. C.

Forensic psychiatry – for mentally abnormal offenders.
PRIVATE: Refer to address and number below.
NHS: Consultant Psychiatrist, Maudsley Hospital,
London SE5 8AZ. Tel: 071 703 6333. Fax: 071 703 0179.

MAJOR DEGREE: *FRCPsych. First qualified in Dublin in 1965. Specialist training at the Middlesex and Broadmoor Hospitals.*

MONTGOMERY, Dr Stuart A.

Recurrent, brief depressions.
PRIVATE: Refer to address and number below.
NHS AND ACADEMIC: Reader and Consultant Psychiatrist,
St Mary's Hospital, Praed Street, London W2 1NY.
Tel: 071 262 1280. Fax: 071 725 6200.

DISTINCTION: President, British Association of
Psychopharmacology. MAJOR DEGREES: MD (Stockholm),
FRCP, FRCPsych. First qualified in London in 1963.
Specialist training at Guy's Hospital, in Stockholm, Sweden;
and at St Mary's Hospital.

MURPHY, Professor Elaine

Especially mental problems of old age.
PRIVATE: Refer to address and number below.
NHS AND ACADEMIC: Professor of Psycho-Geriatric Medicine,
Guy's Hospital, St Thomas Street, London SE1 9RT.
Tel: 071 955 5000.

MAJOR DEGREES: MD, FRCPsych. First qualified in
Manchester in 1971. Specialist training at the Royal London
Hospital.

NOBLE, Dr Peter J.

Especially anxiety and depression.
PRIVATE: 7 Devonshire Place, London W1N 1PA.
Tel: 071 935 4688.
NHS: Consultant Psychiatrist, Maudsley Hospital,
Denmark Hill, London SE5 8AZ.
Tel: 071 703 6333. Fax: 071 703 0179.

MAJOR DEGREES: MD, FRCP, FRCPsych. First qualified in
Cambridge in 1961. Specialist training at the Maudsley
Hospital.

PFEFFER, Dr Jeremy M.

General psychiatry.
PRIVATE: London Medical Centre, 144 Harley Street,
London W1N 1AH. Tel: 071 935 0023.
NHS: Consultant Psychiatrist, Royal London Hospital,
Whitechapel, London E1 1BB.
Tel: 071 377 7000. Fax: 071 377 7396 or 7122.

MAJOR DEGREES: *FRCP, FRCPsych. First qualified (with
honours) in London in 1971. Specialist training at the
Maudsley Hospital.*

PITT, Professor Bryce

Old age.
PRIVATE: Refer to address and number below.
NHS: Consultant in Psychiatry, St Mary's Hospital,
Praed Street, London W2 1NY.
Tel: 071 262 1280 or 725 6666. Fax: 071 725 6200.

ACADEMIC: *Professor in Psychiatry of the Elderly, Royal
Postgraduate Medical School.* MAJOR DEGREES: *MD,
FRCPsych. First qualified in London in 1955. Specialist
training at St Bartholomew's and the Royal London Hospitals.*

RUTTER, Professor Sir Michael.

Problems of adolescence.
PRIVATE: Refer to address and number below.
NHS: Honorary Consultant Physician, Maudsley Hospital,
Denmark Hill, London SE5 8AZ.
Tel: 071 703 6333. Fax: 071 703 0179.

DISTINCTIONS: *Fellow, Royal Society; Honorary Fellow,
British Psychological Society.* MAJOR DEGREES: *MD,
FRCPsych, FRS. First qualified (with distinction) in*

Birmingham in 1955. Specialist training at Queen Elizabeth Hospital, Birmingham and the Maudsley Hospital.
USA: Lately Fellow in Paediatric Psychiatry, Albert Einstein College of Medicine, New York.

SEIFERT, Dr Ruth

PRIVATE: None.
NHS: Consultant Psychiatrist, Hackney Hospital, Homerton High Street, London E9 6BE. Tel: 081 985 5555.

MAJOR DEGREE: FRCPsychn. First qualified in London in 1968. Specialist training at the Maudsley Hospital.

STONEHILL, Dr Edward.

Especially eating problems.
PRIVATE: 138 Harley Street, London W1N 1AH.
Tel: 071 935 0554.
NHS: Consultant Psychiatrist, Central Middlesex Hospital, Acton Lane, Park Royal, London NW1O 7NS.
Tel: 081 965 5733.

DISTINCTION: Lately President, Society for Psychosomatic Research. Major degrees: MD, FRCPsych. First qualified in London in 1961. Specialist training at the Middlesex and St George's Hospitals.

WOOLFSON, Dr Gerald.

Especially anxiety.
PRIVATE: 97 Harley Street, London W1N 1DF.
Tel: 071 935 3400.

NHS: Consultant and Senior Lecturer,
Royal Postgraduate Medical School, Hammersmith Hospital,
Du Cane Road, London W12 0HS.
Tel: 081 743 2030. Fax: 081 740 3139.

DISTINCTION: *Gaskell Gold Medal.* MAJOR DEGREES: *FRCP, FRCPsych. First qualified in Cape Town, South Africa, in 1954. Specialist training at Groote Schuur Hospital, Cape Town and St George's Hospital.*

WELLDON, Dr Estela V.

Especially sexual and social deviancy in women.
PRIVATE: 121 Harley Street, London W1N 1DH.
Tel: 071 935 9076. Fax: 071 586 0713.

DISTINCTIONS: *Lately, Consultant Psychiatrist, University College Hospital. Director of Studies in Forensic Psychiatry, London University. Co-editor,* Revised Applications of Group Analysis and Psychotherapy in Great Britain.
MAJOR DEGREES: *MD, FRCPsych. First qualified in Argentina in 1962. Specialist training at University College Hospital.*

RADIOTHERAPISTS

ARNOTT, Dr Sidney J.

Tumours of the gastrointestinal tract.
PRIVATE: 53 Harley Street, London W1N 1BD.
Tel: 071 323 4331. Fax: 071 636 4596.
NHS: Consultant Radiotherapist, St Bartholomew's Hospital,
West Smithfield, London EC1A 7BE.
Tel: 071 601 8888. Fax: 071 601 7899.

*MAJOR DEGREES: FRCS, FRCR. First qualified in Edinburgh in
1962. Specialist training in Edinburgh.*

COULTER, Dr Carmel.

PRIVATE: King Edward VII Hospital,
Beaumont House, Beaumont Street, London W1N 2AA.
Tel: 071 486 4411.
NHS: Consultant Radiotherapist, St Mary's Hospital,
Praed Street, London W2 1NY.
Tel: 071 262 1280 or 725 6666. Fax: 071 725 6200.

*MAJOR DEGREES: FRCP, FRCR. First qualified in London in
1970. Specialist training at St Bartholomew's Hospital.*

GODLEE, Dr John N.

Bone cancer.
PRIVATE: Cromwell Hospital, Cromwell Road, London SW5
0TU. Tel: 071 370 4233. Fax: 071 370 4063.
NHS: Director, Radiotherapy and Oncology Department,
University College Hospital, Gower Street,
London WC1E 6AU. Tel: 071 387 9300. Fax: 071 380 9977.

*MAJOR DEGREE: FRCR. First qualified in Cambridge in 1955.
Specialist training at the Royal Marsden Hospital. USA: Lately
Research Associate, Stanford Medical Center, California.*

HANHAM, Dr Ian W. F.

Cancer of the head and neck.
PRIVATE: Cromwell Hospital, Cromwell Road, London
SW5 0TU. Tel: 071 370 4233. Fax: 071 370 4063.
NHS: Senior Radiotherapist, Westminster Hospital,
Dean Ryle Street, London SW1P 2AP.
Tel: 081 746 8484. Fax: 081 746 8111.

DISTINCTION: *Consultant in Radiotherapy and Oncology to
the Royal Air Force.* MAJOR DEGREES: *FRCP, FRCR. First
qualified in Cambridge in 1962. Specialist training at the
Westminster Hospital.*

HORWICH, Professor Alan.

Cancer of the testicles.
PRIVATE: Refer to address and number below.
NHS: Consultant Radiotherapist, Royal Marsden Hospital,
Downs Road, Sutton, Surrey SM2 5PX.
Tel: 081 642 6011. Fax: 081 643 0373.

ACADEMIC: *Professor of Radiotherapy, Institute of Cancer.*
MAJOR DEGREES: *PhD, FRCR. First qualified in London in
1971. Specialist training at the Royal Marsden Hospital.*
USA: *Lately Fellow in Medical Oncology, Harvard
Medical School.*

LAMBERT, Dr Joanna.

Gynaecological cancer.
PRIVATE: Refer to address and number below.
NHS: Consultant Radiotherapist, Hammersmith Hospital,
150 Du Cane Road, London W12 0HS.
Tel: 081 743 2030. Fax: 081 740 3169.

MAJOR DEGREES: *MD, FRCR.*

MANTELL, Dr Brian S.

PRIVATE: Refer to address and number below.
NHS: Consultant Radiotherapist, Royal London Hospital,
Whitechapel Road, London E1 1BB.
Tel: 071 377 7000. Fax: 071 377 7396 or 7122.

*ACADEMIC: Senior Lecturer, Heart and Lung Institute. MAJOR
DEGREES: FRCP, FRCR. First qualified in London in 1958.
Specialist training at St George's Hospital.*

PERRY, Dr Nicholas M.

Breast cancer.
PRIVATE: Refer to address and number below.
NHS: Consultant Radiologist, St Bartholomew's Hospital,
West Smithfield, London EC1A 7BE.
Tel: 071 601 8888. Fax: 071 601 7899.

*MAJOR DEGREES: FRCS, FRCR. First qualified in London in
1975. Specialist training at St Bartholomew's Hospital.*

PHILLIPS, Dr Robert H.

Cancer in relation to AIDS.
PRIVATE: Refer to address and number below.
NHS: Consultant in Radiotherapy, Westminster Hospital,
Dean Ryle Street, London SW1P 2AP.
Tel: 081 746 8484. Fax: 081 746 8111.

*MAJOR DEGREES: FRCP, FRCR. Specialist training at the
Westminster Hospital.*

PLOWMAN, Dr P. Nicholas.

Children's cancer.
PRIVATE: 38 Harmount House, 20 Harley Street,
London W1N 1AL.
Tel: 071 631 1632. Fax: 071 323 3487.
NHS: Consultant Physician, Department of Radiotherapy,
St Bartholomew's Hospital, West Smithfield,
London EC1A 7BE. Tel: 071 601 8888. Fax: 071 601 7899.

*MAJOR DEGREES: MD, FRCP, FRCR. First qualified (with
honours) in Cambridge in 1974. Specialist training at
St Bartholomew's Hospital, and in Cambridge.*

PRICE, Dr Patricia.

Gastric, pancreatic and colonic cancer.
PRIVATE: Refer to address and number below.
NHS: Consultant Medical Oncologist,
Hammersmith Hospital, 150 Du Cane Road,
London W12 0HS. Tel: 081 743 2030. Fax: 081 740 3169.

*ACADEMIC: Senior Lecturer in Medical Oncology, Royal
Postgraduate Medical School. DISTINCTION: Sterling Oncology
Award 1989. MAJOR DEGREE: FRCR. First qualified in
Cambridge in 1981. Specialist training at the Royal Marsden
Hospital.*

SPITTLE, Dr Margaret F.

Head, neck and skin cancers.
PRIVATE: Refer to address and number below.
NHS: Director, Meyerstein Institute of Radiotherapy and
Oncology, Middlesex Hospital, Mortimer Street,
London W1N 8AA.
Tel: 071 636 8333. Fax: 071 323 0397.

DISTINCTION: Honorary Consultant Radiotherapist. Royal

Postgraduate Medical School. MAJOR DEGREES: *MSc, FRCR First qualified in London in 1963. Specialist training at the Westminster Hospital and Royal Postgraduate Medical School, London. USA: Lately Instructor, Stanford University Medical Center, California.*

TIMOTHY, Dr Adrian.

Especially Hodgkin's disease and breast cancer.
PRIVATE: 53 Harley Street, London W1N 1DD.
Tel: 071 323 4332.
NHS: Consultant, Department of Radiotherapy,
St Thomas's Hospital, Lambeth Palace Road,
London SE1 7EH. Tel: 071 928 9292. Fax: 071 922 8079.

DISTINCTION: *Lately Hamilton-Fairlie Fellow, St Bartholomew's Hospital.* MAJOR DEGREES: *FRCP, FRCR. First qualified in London in 1969. Specialist training at St Bartholomew's Hospital. USA: Lately Fellow in Radiation Therapy, Harvard Medical School, Boston.*

TOBIAS, Dr Jeffrey S.

PRIVATE: Refer to address and number below.
NHS: Consultant, Radiotherapy Department,
University College Hospital, Gower Street,
London WC1E 6AU. Tel: 071 387 9300. Fax: 071 380 9977.

MAJOR DEGREES: *MD, FRCP, FRCR. First qualified in Cambridge in 1972. Specialist training at St Bartholomew's and the Royal Marsden hospitals. USA: Lately Fellow in Medical Oncology, Harvard Medical School, Boston.*

RHEUMATOLOGISTS

BARNES, Dr Colin G.

Especially Bechet's disease.
PRIVATE: 96 Harley Street, London W1N 1AF.
Tel: 071 486 0967.
NHS: Consultant Physician, Department of Rheumatology,
Royal London Hospital, Whitechapel Road, London E1 1BB.
Tel: 071 377 7000. Fax: 071 377 7396 or 7122.

DISTINCTION: *President, European League Against
Rheumatism.* MAJOR DEGREE: *FRCP. First qualified in London
in 1961. Specialist training at the Royal London Hospital.*

BERRY, Dr Hedley.

PRIVATE: 96 Harley Street, London W1N 1AF.
Tel: 071 486 0967.
NHS: Consultant in Rheumatology and Rehabilitation,
King's College Hospital, Denmark Hill, London SE5 9RS.
Tel: 071 274 6222. Fax: 071 326 3589.

MAJOR DEGREES: *DM, FRCP. First qualified in Oxford in
1967. Specialist training at the Royal London and
St Bartholomew's Hospitals.*

CORBETT, Dr Mary.

PRIVATE: 152 Harley Street, London W1N 1HH.
Tel: 071 935 0444.
NHS: Consultant Physician in Rheumatology,
Middlesex Hospital, Mortimer Street, London W1N 8AA.
Tel: 071 636 8333. Fax: 071 323 0397.

DISTINCTION: *Lately President, Rheumatology Section, Royal*

Society of Medicine. MAJOR DEGREE: *FRCP. First qualified in London in 1957. Specialist training at the Royal Free and the National Hospitals.*

HUGHES, Dr Graham R. V.

Especially connective–tissue disorders.
PRIVATE: Refer to address and number below.
NHS: Consultant Physician, Department of Rheumatology,
St Thomas's Hospital, Lambeth Palace Road,
London SE1 7EH. Tel: 071 928 9292. Fax: 071 922 8079.

ACADEMIC: *Lately Senior Lecturer, Royal Postgraduate Medical School.* DISTINCTIONS: *Head of Lupus Arthritis; Consultant to the Royal Air Force. First qualified in London in 1964. Specialist training at the Royal Postgraduate Medical School, where he was lately a consultant.*

HUSKISSON, Dr Edward C.

PRIVATE: 14a Milford House, 7 Queen Anne Street,
London W1M 9FD.
Tel: 071 636 4278. Fax: 071 323 6829.
NHS: Consultant Physician, St Bartholomew's Hospital,
West Smithfield, London EC1A 7BE.
Tel (direct): 071 606 2435. Fax (direct): 071 606 2351.

ACADEMIC: *Senior Lecturer, St Bartholomew's Hospital.*
MAJOR DEGREES: *MD, FRCP. First qualified in London in 1964. Specialist training at St Bartholomew's Hospital.*

PERRY, Dr Jeremy D.

Especially relating to sporting injuries.
Private: Refer to address and number below.
NHS: Consultant Rheumatologist, Royal London Hospital,
Whitechapel Road, London E1 1BB.
Tel: 071 377 7000. Fax: 071 377 7396 or 7122.

MAJOR DEGREE: FRCP. First qualified in London in 1970.
Specialist training at the Royal London.

SEIFERT, Dr Martin H.

Private: 152 Harley Street, London W1N 1HH.
Tel: 071 935 8868.
NHS: Consultant Physician in Rheumatology,
St Mary's Hospital, Praed Street, London W2 1NY.
Tel: 071 262 1280. Fax: 071 725 6200.

DISTINCTION: Lately President of the Council of Rheumatism
and Rehabilitation. MAJOR DEGREE: FRCP. First qualified in
London in 1964. Specialist training at St Thomas's Hospital.
USA: Lately Fellow in Rheumatology, University of Colorado,
Denver.

WHITE, Dr Anthony G.

Especially electrodiagnosis.
PRIVATE: 152 Harley Street, London W1N 1HH.
Tel: 071 935 8868.
NHS: Consultant Rheumatologist, Royal Free Hospital,
Pond Street, London NW3 2QG.
Tel: 071 794 0500. Fax: 071 435 0143.

ACADEMIC: Senior Lecturer in Clinical Medicine, University
College, London. MAJOR DEGREE: FRCP. First qualified in Bristol
in 1959. Specialist training at University College Hospital.

YATES, Dr D. Anthony.

Especially arthritis of the back.
Private: 26 Devonshire Place, London W1N 1PD.
Tel: 071 935 8917.
NHS: Physician in Charge, Department of Rheumatology,
St Thomas's Hospital, Lambeth Palace Road,
London SE1 7EH. Tel: 071 928 9292. Fax: 071 922 8079.

DISTINCTIONS: *Consultant Rheumatologist to the Army; lately President of the British Society of Rheumatology.* MAJOR DEGREES: *MD, FRCP. First qualified (with honours) in London in 1953. Specialist training at St Thomas's and in the Royal Army Medical Corps.*

TROPICAL PHYSICIANS

BRYCESON, Dr Anthony D. M.

Malaria and infectious diseases including leprosy.
PRIVATE: 26 Devonshire Place, London W1N 1PD.
Tel: 071 580 2475.
NHS: Consultant Physician, Hospital for Tropical Diseases,
4 St Pancras Way, London NW1 0PE. Tel: 071 637 9899.

ACADEMIC: *Senior Lecturer, London School of Hygiene and Tropical Medicine.* MAJOR DEGREES: *MD, FRCP. First quali-fied in Cambridge in 1959. Specialist training in Kenya, Nigeria, and at the London School of Hygiene and Tropical Medicine.*

CHIODINI, Dr Peter.

Parasites.
PRIVATE: Refer to address and number below.
NHS: Consultant Parasitologist, Hospital for Tropical
Diseases, 4 St Pancras Way, London NW1 0PE.
Tel: 071 387 4411.

ACADEMIC: *Senior Lecturer, London School of Hygiene and Tropical Medicine.* MAJOR DEGREES: *PhD, FRCP. First quali-fied in London in 1978. Specialist training in Birmingham and at St George's Hospital. USA: Lately visiting Professor in Parisitology, University of Chicago.*

COOK, Dr Gordon C.

Tropical gastroenterology.
PRIVATE: Refer to address and number below.
NHS: Consultant Physician, Hospital for Tropical Diseases,
4 St Pancras Way, London NW1 0PE.
Tel: 071 387 4411. Fax: 071 383 0041.

ACADEMIC: Senior Lecturer, London School of Hygiene and Tropical Medicine. DISTINCTIONS: Examiner in tropical medicine to London University and the Royal College of Physicians. MAJOR DEGREES: MD, FRCP. First qualified in London in 1957. Specialist training in Papua New Guinea, Zambia and Saudi Arabia.

HALL, Dr Anthony.

Especially malaria and dysentery.
PRIVATE: 7 Wimpole Street, London W1M 7AB.
Tel: 071 580 2846.
NHS: Consultant Physician, Hospital for Tropical Diseases, 4 St Pancras Way, London NW1 0PE.
Tel: 071 387 4411. Fax: 071 383 0041.

DISTINCTIONS: Lately Chief Medical Officer, SEATO; Consultant to Hong Kong Government. MAJOR DEGREE: FRCP. First qualified in London in 1968. Specialist training at the Institute of Tropical Medicine and in Southeast Asia.

McADAM, Professor Keith P.

Especially preventive medicine.
PRIVATE: Refer to address and number below.
NHS AND ACADEMIC: Professor of Tropical Medicine, Hospital for Tropical Diseases, 4 St Pancras Way, London NW1 0PE. Tel: 071 580 2846. Fax: 071 637 4314.

MAJOR DEGREE: FRCP. First qualified in Cambridge in 1970. Specialist training in Papua New Guinea. USA: Lately Associate Professor of Medicine, Tufts University, Boston. DIPLOMAS: American Boards of International Medicine and Allergy and Immunology.

TOMKINS, Professor Andrew M.

Paediatric tropical medicine.
PRIVATE: Refer to address and number below.
NHS: Consultant Physician, Hospital for Sick Children,
34 Great Ormond Street, London WC1N 3JH.
Tel: 071 405 9200. Fax: 071 829 8643.

ACADEMIC: *Professor of International Child Health, Institute of Child Health.* MAJOR DEGREE: *FRCP. First qualified in London in 1966. Specialist training in Nigeria and The Gambia.*

WRIGHT, Dr S. G.

Tropical gastrointestinal infections.
PRIVATE: Refer to address and number below.
NHS: Consultant Physician, Hospital for Tropical Diseases,
4 St Pancras Way, London NW1 0PE.
Tel: 071 580 2846.

MAJOR DEGREE: *FRCP. First qualified in London in 1968. Specialist training at the Medical Research Council and the Hospital for Tropical Diseases.*

UROLOGISTS

CHRISTMAS, Mr Timothy.

Reconstruction of male genitals.
PRIVATE: Refer to address and numbers below.
NHS: Consultant Urologist, Charing Cross Hospital,
Fulham Palace Road, London W6 8RF.
Tel: 081 846 1234. Fax: 081 846 1111.

MAJOR DEGREE: FRCS. First qualified in London in 1980.
Specialist training at University College and the
Royal London Hospitals.

COWIE, Mr Alfred G. A.

Especially urological aspects of tropical diseases.
PRIVATE: 144 Harley Street, London W1N 1AH.
Tel: 071 935 0073. Fax: 071 935 5972.
NHS: Consultant Urologist, University College Hospital,
Gower Street, London WC1E 6AU.
Tel: 071 387 9300. Fax: 071 380 9977.

ACADEMIC: Senior Lecturer, Institute of Urology. MAJOR
DEGREES: FRCS, FICS. First qualified in Cambridge in 1962.
Specialist training at University College and the Royal
Brompton National Heart Hospitals.

DUFFY, Mr Patrick G.

Children's urology.
PRIVATE: Refer to address and number below.
NHS: Hospital for Sick Children, 34 Great Ormond Street,
London WC1N 3JH. Tel: 071 405 9200. Fax: 071 829 8643.

ACADEMIC: Senior Lecturer in Paediatric Urology, Institute of
Urology. MAJOR DEGREE: FRCSI. First qualified in Belfast in
1973.

HENDRY, Mr William F.

Especially male infertility, cancer of the bladder and the testicles.
PRIVATE: 149 Harley Street, London W1N 1HG.
Tel: 071 636 7426.
NHS: Consultant Urologist, St Bartholomew's Hospital,
West Smithfield, London EC1A 7BE.
Tel: 071 601 8888. Fax: 071 601 7899.
and Consultant Urologist, Royal Marsden Hospital,
Fulham Road, London SW3 6JJ.
Tel: 071 352 8171. Fax: 071 351 3785.

ACADEMIC: *Senior Lecturer, Institute of Urology.* MAJOR
DEGREE: *FRCS. First qualified in Glasgow in 1971. Specialist
training at the Royal Infirmary, Glasgow, and St Peter's
Hospital. USA: Mallory Institute of Pathology, Boston,
Massachusetts.*

KIRBY, Mr Roger S.

*Impotence, reconstruction of male genitals, and minimally
interventionist surgery of prostate.*
PRIVATE: 95 Harley Street, London W1N 1DF.
Tel: 071 935 9722.
NHS: Consultant Urologist, St Bartholomew's Hospital, West
Smithfield, London EC1A 7BE.
Tel: 071 601 8888. Fax: 071 601 7899.

DISTINCTION: *Lately Hunterian Professor, Royal College of
Surgeons.* MAJOR DEGREES: *MD, FRCS. First qualified in
Cambridge in 1976. Specialist training at St Thomas's and the
Middlesex Hospitals.*

LLOYD-DAVIES, Mr R. Wyndham.

General urology.
PRIVATE: 53 Harley Street, London W1N 1DD.
Tel: 071 637 9411.
NHS: Senior Consultant Urologist, St Thomas's Hospital,
Lambeth Palace Road, London SE1 7EH.
Tel: 071 928 9292. Fax: 071 922 8079.

ACADEMIC: *Lately Research Fellow, Department of Surgery,
St Thomas's Hospital.* DISTINCTIONS: *Chief Medical Officer
and Consultant Surgeon to the Metropolitan Police; Council
Member, British Association of Urological Surgeons; Vice-
President, Royal Society of Medicine.* MAJOR DEGREES: *FRCS,
MS. First qualified in 1958. Specialist training at St Thomas's
Hospital.* USA: *Lately Research Fellow, San Francisco Medical
Center, University of California.*

MILROY, Mr Ewan J. G.

*Especially stents (bypasses) for urethral strictures and
prostates, and urodynamics.*
PRIVATE: 61 Harley House, Marylebone Road,
London NW1 5HL. Tel: 071 486 6886. Fax: 071 487 4650.
NHS: Consultant Urologist, Middlesex Hospital,
Mortimer Street, London W1N 8AA.
Tel: 071 636 8333. Fax: 071 323 0397.

ACADEMIC: *Senior Lecturer, Institute of Urology.* MAJOR
DEGREE: *FRCS. First qualified in London in 1963. Specialist
training at St Mary's, London, and University Hospital of the
West Indies, Jamaica.* USA: *Lately Research Fellow,
Department of Urology, University of Rochester,
New York State.*

MORGAN, Mr Robert J.

General urology.
PRIVATE: 147 Harley Street, London W1N 1DL
Tel: 071 935 4444. Fax: 071 486 3782.
NHS: Consultant Urological Surgeon, Royal Free Hospital,
Pond Street, London NW3 2QG.
Tel: 071 794 0500. Fax: 071 435 5342.

DISTINCTIONS: *Consultant to St Luke's Hospital for the Clergy, and the Hospital of St John and St Elizabeth.*
ACADEMIC: *Lately Senior Lecturer, Institute of Urology.*
MAJOR DEGREE: *FRCS. Specialist training at St Peter's Hospital.*

MUNDY, Professor Anthony R.

Especially male incontinence and reconstruction of the male genital organs.
PRIVATE: Emblem House, London Bridge Hospital,
27 Tooley Street, London SE1 2PR.
Tel: 071 403 1221. Fax: 071 407 3162.
NHS: Consultant Urological Surgeon, Guy's Hospital,
St Thomas Street, London SE1 9RT. Tel: 071 955 5000.

ACADEMIC: *Professor of Urology, Institute of Urology.* MAJOR DEGREES: *FRCS, MS. First qualified (with honours) in London in 1971. Specialist training at Guy's Hospital. Lately Consultant Surgeon, Force Base Hospital, Muscat, Oman.*

PACKHAM, Mr Derek A.

General urology.
PRIVATE: 48 Wimpole Street, London W1M 7DG
Tel: 071 935 1286.
NHS: Consultant Urological Surgeon, King's College Hospital,
Denmark Hill, London SE5 9RS.

Tel: 071 274 6222.

MAJOR DEGREE: FRCS. *First qualified in London in 1956.*
Specialist training at St Peter's and King's College Hospital.

PARIS, Mr Andrew M. J.

General urology.
PRIVATE: 121 Harley Street, London W1N 1DM.
Tel: 071 486 6324.
NHS: Consultant Urological Surgeon, Royal London Hospital,
Whitechapel Road, London E1 1BB.
Tel: 071 377 7000. Fax: 071 377 7396 or 7122.

MAJOR DEGREE: FRCS. *First qualified in London in 1964.*
Specialist training at St Peter's and the Royal London
Hospitals.

RAMSEY, Mr Jonathan W. A.

Kidney and urological surgery.
PRIVATE: 137 Harley Street, London W1N 1DJ.
Tel: 071 224 3255.
NHS: Consultant Urologist, Charing Cross Hospital,
Fulham Palace Road, W6 8RF.
Tel: 081 846 1234. Fax: 081 846 1111.

MAJOR DEGREE: FRCS. *First qualified in London in 1977.*
Specialist training at St Paul's and St Bartholomew's
Hospitals.

RANSLEY, Mr Philip G.

Children's urology.
PRIVATE: Private Consulting Rooms, 29 Orde Hall Street,

London WC1N 3JL. Tel: 071 405 9791.
NHS: Consultant Surgeon (Urology), Hospital for Sick
Children, 34 Great Ormond Street, London WC1N 3JH.
Tel: 071 405 9200. Fax: 071 829 8643.

ACADEMIC: *Senior Lecturer in Paediatric Urology, Institute of
Child Health. MAJOR DEGREE: FRCS. First qualified in
Cambridge in 1967. Specialist training at the Hospital for Sick
Children and St Peter's Hospital.*

SHEERER, Mr Robert J.

Especially cancer of the bladder and the prostate.
PRIVATE: Parkside Hospital, 53 Parkside, Wimbledon,
London SW19. Tel: 081 946 4204.
NHS: Consultant Urologist, Royal Marsden Hospital,
Fulham Road, London SW3 6JJ.
Tel: 071 352 8171. Fax: 071 351 3785.

ACADEMIC: *Senior Lecturer, St George's Hospital Medical
School and Institute of Cancer Research. MAJOR DEGREE:
FRCS. First qualified in London in 1962. Specialist training at
St Peter's Hospital.*

SNELL, Mr Michael E.

General urology.
Private: Lindoe Wing, St Mary's Hospital, Praed Street,
London W2 1NY. Tel: 071 636 9934.
NHS: Consultant Urologist, St Mary's Hospital,
Praed Street, London W2 1NY.
Tel: 071 262 1280 or 725 6666. Fax: 071 725 6200.

MAJOR DEGREE: *FRCS. Specialist training at St Mary's and
St Peter's. USA: Research Associate, Division of Urology,
Stanford University, California.*

TIPTAFT, Mr Richard C.

Especially the urinary tract, including cancer.
PRIVATE: 134 Harley Street, London W1N 1AH.
Tel: 071 935 0771.
NHS: Consultant Urologist, St Thomas's Hospital,
Lambeth Palace Road, London SE1 7EH.

MAJOR DEGREE: FRCS. *First qualified in London in 1972.*
Specialist training at the Royal London Hospital. USA: Lately
Resident Urologist, Yale University Medical Center.

WHITFIELD, Mr Hugh.

Especially non-surgical treatment of kidney stones, and
minimally invasive genito-urinary surgery.
PRIVATE: 95 Harley Street, London W1N 1DF.
Tel: 071 935 3095.
NHS: Consultant Urologist, St Bartholomew's Hospital,
West Smithfield, London EC1A 7BE.
Tel: 071 601 8888. Fax: 071 601 7899.
and Consultant Urologist, St Mark's Hospital, City Road,
London EC1V 2PS. Tel: 071 253 1050. Fax: 071 601 7973.

MAJOR DEGREES: FRCS, MS. *First qualified in Cambridge in*
1969. Specialist training at St Paul's and St Bartholomew's
Hospitals, and the Royal Postgraduate Medical School.

WILLIAMS, Mr Gordon J.

Especially impotence and cancer.
PRIVATE: Refer to address and numbers below.
NHS: Consultant Surgeon, Urological and Transplant Unit,
Hammersmith Hospital, 150 Du Cane Road,
London W12 0HS. Tel: 081 743 2030. Fax: 081 740 3169.

ACADEMIC: *Senior Lecturer in Urological Surgery, Royal*

Postgraduate Medical School. MAJOR DEGREES: *MS, FRCS. First qualified in London in 1968. Specialist training at Norfolk and Norwich Hospital and the Royal Postgraduate Medical School.*

WITHEROW, Mr Ross O.

General urology.
PRIVATE: 26 Harmont House, 20 Harley Street,
London W1N 1AN.
Tel: 071 935 1252. Fax: 071 637 5373.
NHS: Consultant Urologist, St Mary's Hospital, Praed Street,
London W2 1NY. Tel: 071 262 1280. Fax: 071 725 6200.

First qualified in London in 1968. Specialist training at St Peter's and the Royal London Hospitals. USA: Research Fellow in Urology, San Francisco Medical Center, University of California.

WOODHOUSE, Mr Christopher.

Especially cancer of the bladder, prostate and testes.
PRIVATE: Refer to address and number below.
NHS: Royal Marsden Hospital, Fulham Road,
London SW3 6JJ. Tel: 071 352 8171. Fax: 071 351 3785.

ACADEMIC: *Senior Lecturer, Institute of Urology.*
DISTINCTIONS: *Honorary Consultant, Institute of Urology and Hospital for Sick Children.* MAJOR DEGREE: *FRCS. First qualified in London in 1970. Specialist training at St Peter's and the Royal London Hospitals.*

WORTH, Mr Peter.

Especially incontinence.
PRIVATE: 34 Wimpole Street, London W1M 7AE.
Tel: 071 935 3593.
NHS: Consultant Urological Surgeon, University College
Hospital, Gower Street, London WC1E 6AU.
Tel: 071 387 9300. Fax: 071 380 9977.

ACADEMIC: *Senior Lecturer, Institute of Urology.* MAJOR
DEGREE: *FRCS. First qualified in Cambridge in 1961.*
Specialist training at St Paul's and the Middlesex Hospitals.